ADVENTURES
IN
CANCER LAND

with tips and tools
to guide you

● ● ●

Betsy de Parry

For information about permission to reproduce selections from this book, or about purchasing bulk copies, contact the author at: betsy@candidcancer.com

www.adventuresincancerland.net

LCCN: 2011910450
ISBN: 978-0-615-50248-9

Printed in the USA by Edwards Brothers, Inc.
Ann Arbor, Michigan
www.edwardsbrothers.com

Book design by Lee Lewis Walsh, Words Plus Design
www.wordsplusdesign.com

Cover art by Martyna Alexander

This book is dedicated to

Alex
My biggest cheerleader and the wind beneath my wings

and to

Dr. Mark Kaminski and Judy Estes
Healers who healed me in ways that no medicine ever could

and to

All who went before me and who will follow in my footsteps
My inspiration every day

CONTENTS

PREFACE

December 20, 2001. My husband Alex and I landed in West Palm Beach late that night, happy to take a break from work and the cold Michigan winter. When we boarded the plane to return home several days later, we had no idea that we were heading to Cancer Land, far from our normal life in Ann Arbor, thanks to the fever that was brewing inside me.

Our adventure began like all others: with terrifying news that blinds our eyes, deafens our ears, knots our stomachs and hemorrhages our emotions. No matter how we hear them, the words "you have cancer" are frightening, and I don't know anyone who's ever been ready for ready or not: you have cancer. Alex and I certainly weren't, but cancer quickly plunged us headlong into unfamiliar territory without a compass or a map, much less the time to get our bearings. It cast us into a macabre world of language we often didn't understand, forced us to make choices without fully understanding the consequences, and compelled us to trust my life to total strangers. As if hurled on to a roller coaster, denial, anger, guilt and fear at times propelled us downward at speeds that made us wonder if anything would break our fall. At other times, humor and hope inched us upward.

In the beginning, Alex and I had no clue that Cancer Land would be such an adventure. We'd faced adversity before and cancer was just another bump in the road of life. So certain of that was I that I declared I would write a motivational book full of wit and wisdom. We would soon see that cancer was more like a giant pothole, and no previous experience prepared us for the betrayal we felt when my own body tried to kill me.

It didn't take long to abandon the motivational idea, but I did keep a journal. Although I wrote with no purpose or regularity, writing gave me an outlet for the loneliness and terror I often felt but with which I wanted to burden no one. And lonely I was. Suddenly sick in a healthy world, I desperately wanted to hear from those who had gone before. I wanted to know how they had coped as they morphed from person to patient. How did they maintain their identities? How did cancer affect their daily lives? My questions were endless, but the answers were few because very few survivor stories existed at the time.

Eight months after diagnosis, refractory to two chemo regimens, and on massive doses of steroids, I read my journal in its entirety in the middle of a sleepless night, and I realized — even with less than a fully functioning mind — that recording events and feelings had helped me to interpret the emotions that had so often colored and warped my perspective. Writing, I discovered, had forced me to identify my emotions and ways to cope with them.

With my illness raging and my options dwindling, I began to re-write my journal maniacally, perhaps subconsciously hoping to write the happy ending that I desperately wanted. The first 16 chapters are the result. Chapters 17 and 18 were written as events happened and completed within days of the first anniversary of my diagnosis.

During that time, I began to wonder if sharing our story could help those who would follow in our footsteps. Yet I also realized that our story was just that — ours and ours alone. The circumstances in our life were different from anyone else's. My cancer, its treatments and its side effects were also unique. Even people who underwent the very same chemotherapy had different side effects, some better, some worse. I also wondered if anyone would read the story. After all, Alex and I weren't celebrities, but just ordinary people going about our ordinary lives when we detoured into Cancer Land.

At last, I concluded that while each illness and individual is unique, our story — for someone — might just be the story that I desperately wanted to read when I was first diagnosed. Originally entitled *The Roller Coaster Chronicles*, the first edition was published in 2005 and sold out.

I re-named this edition because our roller coaster ride has long since ground to a halt but our adventures have certainly continued. There's new material that was in my journal but not included in the original edition, which ended near the end of Chapter 19. The next three chapters and all of Part II are entirely new.

Far from the oh-this-is-easy-you-can-do-it book I once declared I would write, Part I is a collage of our adventures in Cancer Land. You'll see that Alex and I arrived at different times, at least emotionally. You'll join us as we were jolted by shock, shaken by worry and fear, went numb, hurt, laughed and cried, tried to pretend life was normal, felt sorry for ourselves, fought and made up — and white-knuckled, held on to each other and to whatever and whomever else we could find, determined to get out of Cancer Land alive. You'll glimpse our problems and solutions, our joys and sorrows, our hopes and frustrations as we grappled with uncertainty, reeled from unexpected blows and pushed doggedly ahead, stabilized by the expertise and caring touch of the health care professionals who cared for me and by the friends and family who supported us.

You'll head with us to Limbo Land, from which we struggled to return to Normal Land. And then we'll all go back to Cancer Land with Alex's mom, which was in many ways much more frustrating and painful, but from which much can be learned.

I believe you'll come to see why Alex and I wholeheartedly believe that good medical care increases the chance for a better outcome, not just physically but also emotionally. I have spared no words of praise for most of those who cared for me — because they deserve it and because they are shining examples of what every person deserves during any type of illness. I'll also introduce you to others who, among other things, nearly pushed Alex and me into emotional freefall without a safety net.

Part II, "Tips and Tools," is a guide to help you navigate through Cancer Land. Each of us has our own adventures, and we experience them in our own ways, but there are many similarities to our adventures, and I hope these travel tips will make yours easier.

Whether you are a patient, caregiver, partner, friend or health care professional, whether you are just beginning this adventure or long past it, Alex and I share our adventures with you, complete with our occasional erratic behavior, with the hope that it will give you insight into the experience of illness and the process of recovery. For patients and partners especially, we hope that you'll find helpful hints to help you *live* in spite of illness and that by seeing some of yourselves in our story, you'll know you aren't alone. Most of all, may you find strength in my recovery and hope that healing is possible.

And if you're just beginning this journey, I'd like to tell you that the road ahead is predictable, but it isn't. There is no road map through Cancer Land, but you'll find many guides along the way. There are no rules of the road. We make them up as we go along. And every one of us travels differently, according to stage and type of cancer, our personalities, our cultural beliefs, and our circumstances, but we share a common beginning. Frightening news is the starting gate where every success story begins, and there are nearly 12 million success stories in America today. May each of us shine as bright beacons of hope for you.

Welcome to Cancer Land.

PART
I

MY ADVENTURES

It always seems impossible until it's done.
— *Nelson Mandela*

1. | CELLS GO WILD

O nce upon a time, my life and yours began as a single cell. Inside its nucleus, some 23 pairs of chromosomes packaged two strands of DNA, the mastermind of all cells. Some 20,000 to 25,000 genes lie scattered along its strands, genes that would eventually make my eyes bluish and my hair brown — the latter, a genetic mistake that was cured by some very good coloring specialists.

But that was years later. In my single cellular life, I couldn't see, hear, think, laugh, or love. But I did one thing very well: I divided, first into two identical cells, and then into four, and then into eight, and so on. No math teacher ever taught me about multiplication by division.

Each new cell became smaller and smaller in order to fit inside the protective bubble that surrounded me. Around day five, some 70 to 100 identical cells crowded inside my bubble, and I was smaller than the period at the end of this sentence. Scientists would call me a blastocyst. I've been called worse.

My cells had unlimited career potential to become any one of the more than 200 types of cells from which every part of my body — my heart, my lungs, my liver, my brain, my blood — would stem. Maybe that's why scientists call them stem cells.

These few generic cells were simply waiting for orders from my genes to give them their specialty, and it didn't take long for my genes to get busy. But genes hold instructions. They don't get their hands dirty any more than general contractors do. Just as general contractors hire plumbers and carpenters and electricians, genes engage the services of proteins to carry out their orders.

By week three of my cellular life, genes were ordering my stem cells to change, or to differentiate, as scientists say. Once they stepped on to the path of specialization, they were segregated into groups of cells for which scientists have very long names. The cells in each group were still able to become a variety of tissues and organs, but not for long. Soon, they would learn their exact specialty and could never go back to being any other type of cell.

Some gathered to form my brain so that I could one day think and learn. Some formed my eyes so that I would be able to see how handsome my husband is. Still others amassed into muscles so that I could reel in a sailfish. Some evolved into nerve cells that would pump out messages so that I could wiggle my toes and smell fresh bread. There would be blood cells to deliver food and oxygen to every corner of my body and rush to protect me from disease and infection. All the while, these specialty cells cranked out identical copies of themselves until just the right number formed all the tissues and organs that made me a human being.

It was an around the clock job. In just nine months, I became a collection of somewhere around five trillion cells, all clones of a single fertilized egg and organized with amazing efficiency to play particular roles. By the time I reached adulthood and looked in a full length mirror, the image of some one hundred trillion cells, give or take, stared back. And the magnitude of information processing activity that goes on inside them puts Intel Pentium to shame.

At any given moment, the frenzied activity inside my body — and yours — almost defies belief. Trillions of cells are constantly working, changing, sending, receiving and responding to signals that alert them to perform their jobs to keep us alive and healthy, and doing all this in harmony, no less. No wonder cells get tired. They take a lot of wear and tear. And as they become less efficient, they divide into new cells and then die off in a very orderly manner in order to maintain the correct number of cells of any given type. At least that's the plan to keep tissues and organs in good working order, and most of the time the system works with amazing accuracy. Sometimes it goes horribly wrong.

Cell division begins in response to a signal on the cell's surface, a signal which tells the tightly coiled DNA to unfold and copy itself. The signal is carried to the nucleus by a series of proteins that form signaling pathways. A mutation anywhere along the pathway means the wrong order is sent. Even when the right one arrives, our cellular copiers can make mistakes, leading to new genes that bark out wrong orders. Fortunately, cellular inspectors halt or destroy the work if not done to their satisfaction — most of the time. Occasionally, mistakes slip past them. Here and there, a few don't seem to matter, but enough mistakes over a period of time can lead to uncontrolled cellular growth: cancer.

My first brush with cellular mistakes occurred when I was 28 and doctors didn't like what they saw on my Pap smear. To prevent suspicious cervical cells from creeping into my uterus, they simply yanked my uterus out, a common practice at the time. End of story. No, end of my uterus. End of cramps and periods. End of children. I thanked God for the one that I had.

Life went on with a few million cells less, but I still had trillions left. And for years, we got along just fine. Old cells divided and died. New ones took over. And cellular mistakes were corrected. Or were they? One day, a single white blood cell — a B lymphocyte, to be exact — divided, and my cellular scribe made a blunder of epic proportions. It incorrectly crossed the 14th and 18th genes, which produced a brand new gene with deadly instructions: it was to generate a protein called BCL2 that told the cell, "Don't die."

What was I doing at the exact moment it happened? Running along a beach? Making love? Maybe I was laughing at a joke that was so funny that my cellular inspectors turned away from their duties to laugh with me. Whenever it was and whatever I was doing, they missed the mistake and the proliferation of immortal cells began. And the irony of it all was that B lymphocytes are part of my immune system — the very system that's designed to protect me from disease, not try to kill me.

It's anybody's guess how long it took for millions of these troublemakers to build up in my body, but build up they did. The first cell with BCL2 copied itself, and its clones divided with wild abandon, but none of them ever died off. And at the cellular level, that was a big problem because cellular death is essential to life: too many cells of the wrong kind crowd out the healthy ones.

I was so active and energetic that I had no idea that bad cells were brewing — at least until the summer of 1999 when they sent their first signal: hot flashes. Suddenly I remembered that the doctor who had relieved me of my uterus all those years ago had warned me that I might have menopausal symptoms. Hmmm. Maybe I should see a gynecologist. Hadn't been to one in twenty-one years. What was left to check?

The gynecologist "confirmed" menopause and quickly wrote a prescription for hormone replacement therapy. She was much too busy to address my concerns about it. Three months later, she was also too busy to address them when I returned for a blood test and followup visit. Another three or four months passed and still I had hot flashes. They were only occasional and not all that bothersome, so I laughed them off as power surges, quit taking the hormones, and never returned to "Dr. Too-Busy-To-Answer-Your-Questions."

The following summer, my cells sent another signal: they swelled up the joints across the tops of my toes and sent searing pain to the balls of my feet. Try walking or standing with that. Some days, I was reduced to staying home and off them.

Fortunately, I worked at home much of the time, but home was surely to blame. My office was on the second floor, our stairs were oak, and I flew barefooted up and down many times during the day, taking two stairs at a time. Surely, landing on the balls of my feet had injured them. A podiatrist quickly agreed and happily sold me some custom-fitted inserts to wear inside shoes, but — *oh dear!* — those inserts didn't fit into a single pair of shoes in my sassy shoe collection, some of which Alex swore I had bought just so no other woman could have them. I had to buy a pair of big, clunky, cushioned shoes that women twice my age wear after they've given up their sassy shoe collections.

I began to take the stairs flat-footed, one at a time, in my new granny shoes. It didn't help one bit, so I ditched the inserts and never went back to "Dr. Sassy Shoe Thief." If I was going to be in pain, anyway, I might as well be wearing cute shoes.

I liked whatever was happening inside my body even less than I liked clunky shoes. In March 2001, I saw a rheumatologist who gave me about sixty seconds of his time, during which he told me I had rheumatoid arthritis, but not a "classic" case because it only affected my feet. He handed me a prescription for methotrexate and a couple of brochures and fled from the room.

The brochures informed me that methotrexate is a form of chemotherapy which can damage certain organs. That wasn't exactly what I had in mind. I wanted to know the underlying cause and how it could be fixed, but I never could get that answer, and it wasn't for lack of asking nicely. Reluctantly, I began the medication, but in no time, felt weak, tired and slightly nauseated occasionally — and still, my feet hurt. I wanted to know other options, but I could never find out from "Dr. Do-As-I-Tell-You-And-Don't-Ask-Any-Questions." Within weeks, I quit the methotrexate and — *surprise!* — all the physical symptoms vanished except the one I'd started with. And one was enough.

By early summer, another doctor also thought I had rheumatoid arthritis but not a "classic" case. Rather than shoving chemotherapy drugs at me, he felt that nutritional changes could possibly keep me off them. That sounded much better, so I eliminated all dairy products from my diet and made other minor changes that Dr. Holistic suggested.

My feet really did improve. They weren't pain free all the time, but the improvement was significant and I was pleased that my body and I were beginning to cooperate again. At least I wanted to believe that we were. Intuition occasionally gnawed at me, raising doubts about menopause and arthritis, but it never occurred to me that I was on a collision course with cancer. How was I to know that hot flashes were symptomatic of lymphoma or that the pain and swelling in my feet were signs of my immune system shorting out? That obviously didn't occur to the four doctors I saw either.

● ● ●

The task ahead of us is never as great as the power behind us.
— *Ralph Waldo Emerson*

2. | CANCER CALLS

D ecember 30, 2001. Alex and I were vacationing in West Palm
Beach. My feet had behaved beautifully in sassy sandals since
our arrival, but that afternoon, my mischievous cells sent the
third signal: fever. When it began, I was shopping at a mall with my
daughter Juli and grandchildren, two-and-a-half-year-old Skye and
ten-month-old Nicholas. Exhausted, I went straight to bed when we
returned to our condo, assuming that I had picked up a little bug
from the kids.

By morning the fever had broken, but it returned each subsequent afternoon, and my thighs felt weak and achy. Certain that I
had some type of flu or virus, Alex bought a variety of tonics, but
nothing worked. A little voice inside me started whispering, "Better
check this out." If I had tried to explain the voice, Alex would have
thought I had lost my mind.

Alex, my low-grade fever and I flew home on January 3. As we
walked through the airport, my legs felt so weak that I feared they
would crumble. At baggage claim, all the chairs were occupied so I
collapsed on the floor while Alex retrieved the luggage.

I knew I needed medical help, but never one to haul myself in
for regular inspections, I didn't know any doctors except the four I'd

recently seen, and they couldn't even eliminate hot flashes or pain. The morning after we arrived home, I called a family practice group. They could see me in March. "And just what shall I do if the fevers continue?" I asked. "Go to the emergency room," a cold voice answered.

When my temperature spiked to 103 later that day, that's exactly what I did. Unable to reach Alex, I jumped in my car and headed to the University of Michigan's Emergency Room, a fifteen minute drive from home. Yes, I'd like to think that Independent is my middle name, but the truth is, I was scared. Alex and I finally connected as I neared the hospital. "U of M is a trauma center. You'll spend all night there." He suggested I turn around and go to the corner emergency clinic.

I was aggravated that he would even suggest the corner clinic. That little voice inside my head was screaming, "You need to be at U of M. Don't go anywhere else." Alex joined me at the emergency room, annoyed that I had shown up at a trauma center on a Friday night for a little fever.

I spent the next twelve hours in the emergency room. About halfway through the summary of potential culprits, Dr. Eric Ketcham, a third year resident, casually said something about cancer, but assured me that it was very unlikely. For definitive answers, we'd have to wait for test results. I returned home, certain that nothing was wrong that couldn't easily be fixed. Otherwise Dr. Ketcham would have admitted me to the hospital. Right?

Though exhausted, I was at least fever-free in the mornings, and I wasn't about to let a little fatigue interfere with my normal routine. On Monday morning, January 7, I got in my car and headed to our tile supplier, some forty-five minutes away. And that's when cancer sent me on a very distant detour from normal.

It was just before ten that morning when cancer called. I was nearing the Silver Lake exit on US 23 just north of Ann Arbor when my cell phone rang. It was Dr. Ketcham calling to inform me that tests indicated cancer. I might as well have been hit by the semi that was traveling next to me. I'll never pass that exact spot again without thinking about the phone call that abruptly interrupted my life. Dr. Ketcham first asked if I was at a place we could talk. Of course, I told him, failing to mention that I was behind the wheel on a busy highway. He presented the facts respectfully and calmly. My white blood counts were high. He suspected lymphoma. I should see a specialist right away. He might as well have said, "Good morning, Betsy. I'm calling to bring you a message of terror. And if you think cancer is hard on your body, just wait until you see what it does to your psyche. I suggest you and your family equip yourselves with emotional yo-yos with l-o-n-g elastic strings. You'll need them." Of course no doctor would ever be so blunt. At least I hope not.

Dr. Ketcham was still talking when I pulled off onto the shoulder wondering what happened to that "unlikely" scenario he had assured me just three days earlier. I'm not certain how long I sat there after we hung up. I didn't cry. I just sat, oblivious to everything around me. What are you supposed to, I wondered, when a total stranger announces that cancer has called upon you? Curiously, I wondered how doctors psych themselves up to make those calls.

My surroundings slowly came back into focus. Cars and trucks were whizzing by and a sign on a church beside the road jolted me, I hoped not prophetically. "Free trip to heaven. Details inside," it said. I shuddered and decided to call Alex. He always had answers for everything, but then, all he could think to say was, "Stay there. I'll come get you."

"That doesn't make sense," I replied. "We'd have to come back to get my car." I assured him I was fine to drive, but heading home, my head was spinning and yet I was numb. How had I gone from choosing tile to choosing an oncologist in the span of just minutes? It felt like the mother of bad Mondays.

Alex worked the phone, calling doctors we knew at the University of Michigan (U of M). Before I arrived home, he had reached one of them who knew that U of M had a clinic that specialized in lymphoma, and our friend would call to see about getting us in right away.

I pulled into the garage and walked into the kitchen. Everything was just as I had left it, but the house looked different. Felt different. I felt detached from everything that was familiar. I wandered from room to room, scanning all the family photographs scattered about. I desperately wanted to feel connected to the people in those photographs, for they were part of my past, my present and my future. At least I'd always counted on them being part of my future. Suddenly I wasn't so sure I had one. Don't be a drama queen, I thought. This is just a bad dream.

Surely nothing so horrible as cancer would sabotage our lives now. We'd both endured various challenges in our lives, but at the moment life was good. No, it was great. Alex and I had known each other a dozen years, lived together for six and a half, and been married for just over three. Thirty-one years earlier he'd started a home-building company. I had sold homes all my adult life in West Palm Beach. Smitten, I'd traded my sandals for boots and joined him in Ann Arbor where I went to work with him.

Wandering through the house, I thought about how great our life had been until an hour earlier. We'd just completed a successful year, were financially stable, enjoyed a blissful marriage, and had plenty of optimism and energy. Who could ask for more?

I became angry. Angry that anything would dare to intrude on our busy, happy life. Angry that my plans for the morning had changed. I had things to do, people to see, places to go. It was a new year, and I had plenty of goals to accomplish. With plans to begin a large residential development later that year, I had no time for medical tests, much less a major illness. Cancer was definitely not a part of my new year's resolution.

But of course I wasn't ill. It wasn't possible. Alex arrived home, put his arms around me and assured me he was as certain as I that this was just a mistake. Of course it was. No one in my family had ever had cancer. Strokes were the culprit in our genes, not the Big C.

Nevertheless, someone from the lymphoma clinic would look at the tests and call us late in the afternoon.

As fever began to brew again, I collapsed, exhausted, on the couch, from which I ranted and raved to Alex, "I will NOT have cancer." That day would be the first of many that he would be my lightning rod, attempting to ground me against my own highly charged emotions. It wasn't long before he simply could absorb no more voltage.

The phone finally rang late in the afternoon. A calm, kind, compassionate voice told me that she had looked at the tests taken at the emergency room and felt that a more specialized test — flow cytometry — would be necessary to confirm the suspicion of lymphoma. Confirm? Good — that implied it could also deny the suspicion. Could I come in tomorrow? Absolutely. Whatever flow cytometry was, I was sure it would prove the initial suspicions wrong, and the sooner I had that proof, the sooner I could get back to life.

That calm voice belonged to Judy Estes, Nurse Practitioner and Lymphoma Program Coordinator. The clinic specializes in the diagnosis and treatment of all the various kinds of blood cancers. Using a team approach, each case is reviewed by a group of highly trained specialists, including hematologists/oncologists, radiation oncologists, surgical oncologists, pathologists, nurse practitioners, physician's assistants and oncology nurses. Together, like five star generals convening in a war room, they evaluate each patient's individual case and develop a carefully coordinated treatment plan. At the time, I had no way of knowing that so much brainpower would eventually evaluate my case.

By week's end, the fever had stopped, my feet didn't hurt, and I hadn't had a hot flash all week. How could anything possibly be wrong? That's when Judy called with the news that the flow cytometry test confirmed suspicions. She had already made an appointment for me to see Dr. Mark Kaminski the following week.

There's no getting used to hearing, "You have cancer." In fact, hearing it from Judy was worse because I'd gone from *possibly* having cancer to *probably* having cancer. When Judy and I hung up, I put my elbows on the kitchen counter and buried my head in my hands. This can't be happening, I thought. My test must have been switched with someone else's. Or someone misread the results. I *can't* have cancer. Then why did I feel so scared?

After several minutes, I hauled myself upstairs to dress for the homebuilder association's annual awards banquet that evening. I stepped into the shower and stood motionless under the running water for a very long time. My whole body felt weighted by a single thought: I *can't* have cancer.

I couldn't have heard Alex arrive home, and I didn't hear him come into the bathroom until he was knocking on the shower door. "Hey, you gonna save me any hot water?" he asked.

I just stood there, looking at him through the glass. I could tell by his face that he knew something was wrong. I turned off the water, wrapped a towel around me, stepped out of the shower, and sat down on the edge of the whirlpool. "What is it?" Alex asked.

I stared at the floor, unable to answer him. I tried, but I couldn't complete a single sentence I started. He got the message and reminded me that we hadn't yet seen the doctor. Test results could be wrong. There were surely more tests that would disprove that flow-whatever-it-was. And if I wanted to stay home that evening, it would be fine with him.

No, we would go out. I thought it would help to get our minds off the news, but I sat semi-catatonic through most of the evening, hardly hearing the lively laughter and conversation that filled the room. Alex even had to nudge me when my name was called for an award.

The following morning, I decided to organize the piles of papers that had accumulated in my office, but I had to make room for them by cleaning out file cabinet drawers that were bursting at the seams. A bottom drawer housed a collection of miscellaneous papers that I had saved, thinking that they might someday be useful. All related to real estate or construction — ads I had once liked, copies of real estate contracts from other areas of the country, and such. I threw many of them away to make room for more papers I would probably never need.

I came to the very last file, wedged at the back of the drawer. Across the top I had written "Jokes and Miscellaneous." I laughed at some of the jokes I hadn't seen in years. And then I came to the very last piece of paper, a copy of an article on thermal fax paper, faint but still legible. I think my heart almost stopped. I know I got a cold chill. And I shrieked so loudly that Alex ran upstairs to see what was going on. In bold letters, the title of the article proclaimed "Curing Cancer," and it was about a new breakthrough pioneered by none other than Dr. Mark Kaminski.

I had completely forgotten about the article, but I did remember how it came into my possession. In the fall of 1996, Alex and I were working in a Detroit suburb. One of our colleagues had a friend who was diagnosed with lymphoma. She had heard of an article about a cancer breakthrough at U of M and thought that it had been printed in the *Observer*, a monthly magazine about Ann Arbor. We hadn't seen it, so we called the *Observer* and someone faxed it right over. I must have made a photocopy for our colleague. I certainly didn't remember keeping the original fax.

And why did I? I never, ever kept articles that were unrelated to our business or interests. Cancer obviously has nothing to do with the homebuilding industry, and I assure you it doesn't fall under the category of hobbies and interests. Keeping that article was one thousand per cent out of character for me. Don't try to convince me there isn't a higher being.

Five and a half years after pulling the article off the fax machine, I read it. But first I stared at the faded picture of Dr. Kaminski, glad to know at least what he looked like. A tiny part of me wondered if he would soon be my savior. Of course not. There was nothing to save me from.

Dr. Kaminski had developed a new drug called Bexxar which treated lymphoma using a radiolabeled antibody. I didn't completely understand the concept, but I did grasp its success. Cure, the article said, was possible with this new treatment. Surely, five and a half years after its printing and a few clinical trials later, this new drug would get rid of lymphoma — which, of course, I couldn't possibly have.

Alex and I read and re-read the article. I wanted to toss it out along with the pile of papers I was discarding, but I just couldn't. Something made me place it in its own notebook, which would soon be filled with information about lymphoma.

Closing the file cabinet, I grew annoyed. Annoyed that a couple of medical tests were interfering with my busy schedule. Fear soon followed — fear of what I was certain was an overworked, understaffed health care system where no one would care that I have a name and a life that matters, at least to me. Would I be reduced to a patient number and a statistic, just one of thousands of people who pass through the revolving doors hoping to be made good as new?

● ● ●

The University of Michigan Health System is a huge complex of massive buildings, more massive now than the 4.67 million square feet massive it was in 2002. That's equivalent to about 107 acres. And I was supposed to navigate around the place? Right.

I'd only been in the hospital once, a few years earlier when my mother came down with pneumonia while she was visiting us. The first time my sister and I went to see her after she was admitted from the emergency room, we got thoroughly lost in those vast buildings. Down corridor after corridor, through door after door, we wandered straight into one of the lab areas.

And not just any lab. Caged monkeys lined the walls of the one we wandered into. Astounded, my sister and I looked at them, looked at each other, closed the door, and without a word, ran. And I mean *ran*. Some distance down the hall, we stopped, hardly believing what we had seen.

"I want to rescue every one of those poor animals," I said. "Do you think we can get them out of here without being noticed?" We both knew the answer. "Mother's not *here*, and this place gives me the creeps," I added.

Poor animals. From that day forward, when I drove past the hospital, I thought about those poor monkeys and could hardly bear to ponder what might happen to them. Suddenly, I feared that I might become just another monkey. Surely no one would see me as a human being with feelings. What would I matter to anyone so long as I gave over my body to research? It obviously hadn't occurred to me that research — with the help of mice and monkeys — prolongs human life.

I was a little defensive by the time our appointment came. Alex drove to that part of the hospital complex where a big sign directed us to the "Cancer and Geriatrics Center." The sign might as well have said, "Betsy, you'll have to graduate from cancer before you get to geriatrics." I tried to make jokes about being an antique, but Alex wasn't amused. Silently, I wondered how many strangers would have to see me naked. I had neither aspired to become a middle-aged Gypsy Rose Lee nor did I want to submit to degrading and disgusting — or painful — procedures.

The waiting area seemed like a holding pen for a variety of people of all ages, from children to seniors, who were at various stages of disease and treatment. Some were in wheelchairs. Some wore scarves, hats, various bandages and surgical masks. Most looked tired and resigned. What horrors were happening to those poor souls, I wondered. I couldn't possibly belong in their midst.

And just what were Alex and I doing in a cancer clinic? We'd always been so healthy. Yet there we sat, together with our personalities, our beliefs, our fears, and our expectations, although Alex wasn't certain what to expect. At least I had made the acquaintance of waiting rooms and doctors and hospitals during my parents' illnesses, but Alex had never confronted so much illness in one place. Many months later, he would tell me that the magnitude of human suffering stared at him from the faces of the patients in that room and that the toll of human illness became a terrible and frightening reality for him. It was indeed a frightening, foreign place that looked like the land of loss and grief. And I didn't even know where the bathrooms were.

In the examining room, I donned the gown of patienthood. It wouldn't take long to learn that the ties never match up — *ever*. I looked at Alex and admitted, "I'd rather be anywhere than here. This can't be happening."

"That's exactly what I was thinking," Alex replied, fidgeting with his wedding ring.

Judy arrived and examined me. She was a pretty woman with short hair, large eyes that communicated compassion, and an energetic and professional manner. She was as warm and kind in person as she had been on the phone, and I liked her instantly. Still, I'd had enough. I didn't have time for cancer and I wasn't about to trust perfect strangers, especially doctors who would bolt through the door, ask a question or two — if I was lucky — and bolt out just as quickly. No matter who came into the examining room, I was ready to wallop anyone who tried to prolong this little scare.

And then I met a doctor unlike any I'd ever met: Dr. Mark Kaminski. And he almost disarmed me. Almost. He strode into the room wearing a friendly smile and genteel manner. He sat down, looked us squarely in the eye, and with his calm and steady voice, began to talk about lymphoma. Intuitively knowing that we had no idea what questions to ask, he answered all the ones he knew we would need answers to. In fact, he gave us more information than I could possibly absorb. Among other things, he told us that the disease presents itself in a variety of ways and that the fever, the pain in my feet and hot flashes were probable symptoms.

Much to my amazement, Dr. Kaminski never seemed to be in any hurry. He didn't treat me like a monkey. And his gentle eyes and patient explanations, delivered unhurriedly with reassuring authority and compassion, almost persuaded me that he had aced his

"Bedside Manner" course back in medical school. My urge to wallop fizzled down but not out. After all, this was the third explanation for my symptoms in a year and a half, and the other four doctors had been wrong. No matter how nice Dr. Kaminski was, surely he could be wrong, too.

And I wasn't convinced that he fully grasped how important life was to me, though I suspected that if I really had cancer — which I didn't believe that I did — that I would need a doctor who would believe with all his heart that I would live — and a doctor whom I could trust, with whom I could communicate, and who would deliver good news or bad compassionately, honestly and quickly. Of course I also wanted that same compassionate doctor to be a ruthless assassin who would gleefully kill any cancer cells that might be mistakenly breeding inside me. Would this Dr. Kaminski be my Dr. Jekyll and Mr. Hyde? At the time, Alex and I didn't have any idea how lucky we were to be sitting with one of the world's foremost lymphoma experts.

I was determined to get an answer to the only question I had, which was how long I had to live — *if* I had lymphoma. Reluctant to share that little tidbit, Dr. Kaminski instead tried to assure me that statistics don't predict an individual's outcome. That was no answer, so I pushed. Big mistake. I would be doing some serious mental gymnastics to forget that the median time from diagnosis to death was eight years for the type of lymphoma Dr. Kaminski suspected.

As soon as he said it, I wanted to throw myself at his feet and beg for a guarantee that he would propel me to the far side of the median — a lifetime on the far side — just in case I really had lymphoma. Hadn't the article said he had found a cure?

Dr. Kaminski repeated what he had already said: that there were many promising new treatments on the horizon and he wanted us to leave his office with hope. I hoped, all right — that he was wrong.

Before our visit concluded, Dr. Kaminski made arrangements for me to have a CT scan and invited a surgeon to join us. Together, they examined me and spoke "Medicalese," in which I was not fluent. I did, however, understand that a biopsy would conclusively confirm suspicions. At least I knew what a biopsy was. Dr. Chang, the surgeon, would cut me open, remove a small piece of me, a pathologist would look at it, see nothing wrong, and this little scare would end. Period.

Alex, reserved and quiet by nature, had scarcely said a word throughout our appointment, and he said even less as we walked hand in hand to the car. Finally I said lightly, "Hey, don't look so glum. A couple of doctors just want to carve me up a little. So let's humor them and show them I'm fine, okay?"

"Okay," Alex agreed, trying to smile. "If they want to biopsy, the good news is that the doctors must not be sure you have lymphoma. Maybe they think there's a mistake, too." A year later, he would tell me that he added silently, "But what if the biopsy confirms their suspicions? Then what?"

• • •

A wise man adapts himself to circumstances as water
shapes itself to the vessel that contains it.
— *Chinese proverb*

3. | JUDGE AND JURY

The fevers stopped, but my body acquired its own 48-hour rhythm. One day it stayed awake throughout the day. The next day it required an hour or two nap, although require is an understatement. It was impossible to stay awake through the drowsy spells. At least the hot flashes came in handy during the cold Michigan winter.

A few days after meeting Dr. Kaminski, Alex asked if I felt up to going to a show in a convention center. I didn't feel like walking around, so I waited for him by the food court where I promptly put my head on the table and fell asleep. Forty-five minutes later he found me there, snoozing in public. "Geez, Alex, was I snoring?"

"Just drooling," he teased.

Our family was concerned about me, and we decided to tell them everything we knew. It was like downplaying a nuclear attack.

We didn't ask anyone to research lymphoma, but a couple of days after sharing the news, I woke up one morning to find an email from one of our family members. It said, "Have been researching lymphoma. You have a fifty percent chance of survival." Stunned, I stared at the computer screen for what seemed an eternity. We didn't even know if I had lymphoma, and we certainly hadn't considered death and dying. I almost replied, "Have been researching life. You have a zero percent chance of survival."

Instead, ranting and raving, I flew into the bathroom where Alex was just getting out of the shower. "This is bull," I squawked. "Nobody has a fifty percent chance of survival. Everybody has a one hundred percent certainty of dying. Nobody wants to admit it. And I'll be damned if I'll let some email inform me of my odds. My odds are as good as yours — we're all gonna die from something. And lymphoma will not get me." I carried on about the possibility of living to be one hundred and dying of natural causes and of not knowing how much time any one of us has on this earth. Wrapped in a towel, Alex just stood there, arms by his side, enduring my fury. And then, without a word, he put his arms around me. Need I say that research assistants, especially self-appointed ones, should share only that information which might actually be useful?

Under normal circumstances, I could easily brush off insensitive comments, but I would soon learn that there is nothing normal about having cancer nor it is so easy to brush them off when we do. I never made a conscious decision to build a protective shield around myself, and until many months later, I didn't realize that I had, but I think that email was when I began. From that day forward, I did everything possible to avoid anyone whose stupid comments dashed my hopes, including the person who sent that message, which wasn't too difficult since she lived out of state and I was *always* asleep when she called. Yep, Alex and the answering machine had my back.

● ● ●

Picture Day arrived, and Alex chauffeured me to the hospital for the scan. We were both on edge. Summoning a smokescreen for our fears, we quibbled about which hospital entrance to use.

Again we found ourselves in a holding pen staring at the faces of illness. Perhaps others were thinking the same of me, adorned as I was in hospital couture. As I left the holding pen for my picture, I quipped to Alex over my shoulder, "I'll tell them to get my good side. Shall we order the 8 x 10's or the wallets?" He didn't even smile. My first glimpse of the machine reminded me of a big doughnut. There was a hole through which I would slide while the machine snapped pictures. But first I was shot up with iodine, a dye that would help whoever was looking to better see whatever it was they wanted to see. I smiled for the camera and slid through the machine as the taste of iodine flooded my mouth. No one warned me that would happen. Bon Appetit.

The following day, I gave some thought to the word lymphoma. There was brain cancer. Breast cancer. Prostate cancer. Lung cancer. Liver cancer. Bone cancer. They were bad because every one of them actually included the word cancer. I decided that I should be worried if lymphoma were called lymphoma cancer. But it wasn't. Unattached to the "C" word, lymphoma couldn't be too bad. Right?

I even made a rhyme out of it — nymphoma — and jokingly put Alex on performance notice in case I became a "nymphomaniac." He was unamused by my mockery of a serious disease, but ah, denial and mirth are fabulous stressbusters.

I also decided that I was emotionally equipped for the challenge if I had "nymphoma." After all, I had faced adversity before. Several years earlier, my world had instantly changed when my former husband had decided one day to drop out of life. Any security, financial or otherwise, I had ever thought I had was completely obliterated. Among other things, the IRS was not amused that he had failed to pay our income taxes, and I was left to clean up the mess. Four years and lots of hard work later, I had resolved matters and started over, albeit battered and bruised and convinced that the IRS was a masterpiece of bureaucracy and redundancy.

And there was the time that I was driving down the street in a perfectly decent part of West Palm Beach when two teenage gang members emptied their guns. My car was badly injured, but I was unharmed — at least physically. Several months later, I walked away from that fiasco convinced that the justice system was a masterpiece of hypocrisy. Why else would they lock up juries and set criminals free?

Yes sirree, I knew what it was like for life to change in an instant. I knew how to handle adversity. I knew what it was like to be up and to be down, emotionally and financially. I knew how to face cold, impersonal bureaucratic agencies, and I was still certain — no matter how nice Dr. Kaminski and Judy had been — that the health care system was just another bureaucracy. I'd had experience, I told myself, and could cope with any challenge. I am woman. Hear me roar. Little did I know how quickly my roar would dwindle to a whimper.

● ● ●

Less than three weeks after Dr. Ketcham's call, Alex and I left for the hospital before dawn on a cold, dark, snowy morning. My spirits were high because I was determined to believe that this test — the biopsy — would conclusively prove that I was fine. And I was willing to be drugged and knifed to prove it. Wasn't I the martyr?

At outpatient surgery, I again slipped into the gown of patienthood, thinking that hospitals have one-size-fits-all gowns for no other reason than to reduce individuals to one-description-fits-all: patient. Deprived of individuality, how easy then to further reduce people to a record of symptoms. I wanted to tell the hospital that one size does not fit all and that patients surely have color preferences as well. I rambled on to Alex that Calvin Klein could do wonders for these blah uniforms. Surely he would use different colors, and of course he would make them in different sizes. And while he was at it, he'd make sure that the ties matched up.

An IV was inserted into my arm, and I began to get a little sleepy. Alex kissed me as I was wheeled away. I was sorry that this was taking time from his busy schedule, but it would all be over soon.

The operating room felt colder than a winter day in Antarctica. Hypothermia, here I come, I thought, as one nurse fastened my legs to the table while two others stretched out and strapped down my left arm. For everyone in that room but me, it was just a routine day at the office — an office in which I was voluntarily allowing myself to be drugged and clamped to a metal table surrounded by strangers wielding knives. "What's wrong with this picture?" was my last thought.

Still in the operating room, I awoke. The overhead lights were bright, and people seemed to be scurrying around. I asked Dr. Chang if he would show me what he had removed, and he placed a small vial before my sleepy eyes. Floating in it was what looked like a bloody pea.

At that moment, I realized the significance of The Pea. It would determine my future. The Pea knew whether or not I would live to dance at my grandchildren's weddings. The Pea knew whether or not I would grow old along with Alex. Who was going to look at that bloody pea and interpret just what it had to say? Somebody I had never even met? Somebody who didn't know how much I wanted to live? Somebody who had maybe just had a fight with his wife? I wanted to bolt off that operating table and hand deliver my bloody pea to the pathologist. I wanted to look him or her in the eye and beg, "This belongs to me. It's the key to my life. Please, oh please, let me live."

It occurred to me that I would be placing blind faith in people I would never know if I really had cancer. There would be people who would interpret x-rays, CT scans, and who knew what else. Lying there on the table, I panicked, wondering if these people realized how profoundly their reports impact people's lives. I desperately needed to meet these invisible prognosticators and to plead with them to remember that I, like them, am a human being with hopes and dreams and a family. But of course I couldn't meet any of them. I simply had to place my faith in their experience and my hope in their perfection. Though ordinarily a trusting soul, I felt so vulnerable by having no other choice but to place blind trust in people I would never meet.

And just how would blood tests, CT scans or biopsies measure my emotions? Would the pathologist reading the bloody pea also calculate my fear? Would he send a report to Dr. Kaminski that said, "Betsy has such and such type and stage of lymphoma. And by the way, her fear factor is off the charts"? Of course not. The medical experts would be interested only in the parts of me that they could put into test tubes and vials or see under microscopes, on slides or on film. I wanted to scream, "But that's only a little part of me. Don't forget the important parts — the ones that make me laugh and cry and love." I doubted anyone would have listened to that plea.

I was the first to return to the recovery room, which was large and empty except for Alex. I was so happy to see him. What had he been thinking while I was away? He wouldn't say, but he held my hand tightly. Months later he would confide that he had worried about a stranger cutting into me while he sat isolated and unable to protect me should anything go wrong during the surgery. He smiled sheepishly when, half chuckling, I wondered out loud how a builder was supposed to help out in an operating room.

He also hoped that there had been a mix-up, but began to prepare himself for the possibility that I may in fact have lymphoma. Still, he convinced himself that it couldn't possibly be so bad since I neither looked nor acted sick. Sure, he had noticed the lethargy, but he'd also noticed that the fevers had stopped — surely a sign of improvement. Even if the biopsy showed some kind of lymphoma, he told himself that — if we had to — we would deal with this quickly and go on with our life.

My ticket to freedom was stable vital signs and an empty bladder. As a nurse helped me to the bathroom, IV pole in tow, I couldn't help but think how ridiculous I must look shuffling across the room in non-skid socks, a gown that ten of me could fit into and a paper hat hiding my hair. And forbidden as I was to wear my contacts or makeup, my naked face and glasses completed the ensemble. Not exactly power clothes.

I hated for Alex to see me this way. Sure, he saw me every morning at my worst, but this was worse than my worst. The very surroundings, the IV pole, the absurd outfit — all stripped away the me we knew. If I could just find my funny face, Alex would recognize the old me. As I exited the bathroom, he sat at my bedside hunched on the edge of a chair, pulling his wedding ring up to his knuckle and pushing it back again. I put on a big grin, took the IV pole in both hands and began to twirl around with my new dance partner, Mr. I. V. Pole. Alex jumped to his feet and ran toward me mumbling something about falling. "Oh Alex, you need to lighten up and have a little fun," I teased. Again, he didn't smile.

I had not met my own expectations during the month of January, and my frustration was escalating. Lying on the couch for hours on end, napping, running fever, and spending far too much time having medical tests left little time to accomplish what I had set out to do. Alex, who has always given himself more tasks every day than anyone can possibly complete, was doing everything possible to do his job and mine, which became an increasing source of worry for me, not to mention guilt.

When I returned home from the biopsy, I determined that I must make up in February what I had failed to do in January. I'd completed the medical tests, and surely this nightmare would soon be over. Then why did I feel like a defendant whose judge and jury were about to render my verdict? I prayed I'd be found innocent of all charges.

• • •

It takes as much energy to wish as it does to plan.
— *Eleanor Roosevelt*

4. | THE QUEEN OF DENIAL

few days after the CT scan and biopsy, Alex and I waited in the examining room for Dr. Kaminski, still hoping that nothing was wrong. Our hope waned when he reported the verdict: low grade, follicular small-cleaved lymphoma, grade I, non-Hodgkin's, stage IV. What a mouthful. And worse — there was neither a stage V nor a cure.

My white blood counts were soaring. Dr. Kaminski discussed various treatment options should my counts continue to rise. "Watch and wait," a period when no treatment is administered, was probably not an option for long, he stated. When he mentioned chemotherapy, all I heard was the sound of vomiting. He talked about clinical trials. Bexxar was still under FDA review, so his magic cure was not yet available. He was clearly moving me in a direction I did not want to take. But with false bravado, I joked to him, "Well, let's fix this fast. Dead salesmen don't usually meet their quotas, and my boss might get upset." Dr. Kaminski smiled. Alex was horrified. The wisecrack kept me from sobbing.

The problem was that there was no fixing this fast, if at all. At best, chemotherapy — my only option at the time — would slow the disease, but sooner or later, it would return and require stronger drugs. Then the whole cycle would repeat, and remission periods would decrease with each subsequent treatment until no options remained. No wonder I feared that I would be spending my future undergoing a series of treatments, each more debilitating than before. And there was that little issue of the median life span of eight years that meant I would never see our grandchildren get married. All I could do was hope that a better treatment would come along. At least there were some in the pipeline, including Bexxar, on which I pinned my hope.

But that didn't help then. From the moment we left the examining room until we arrived in the lobby, my eyes stared straight down at my feet. There was a basketball-size lump in my throat, and I knew I would cry if I looked up at anyone, especially Alex. We had met at the hospital, and he asked if I would like to go with him and return for my car later. "No," I mumbled, "I'm okay." He knew I wasn't, and he put his arm around me. I buried my head in his shoulder and cried, "I just wanted Dr. Kaminski to say everything was okay. I want this to go away and leave us alone."

Tears flowed gently down my cheeks. Alex put his other arm around me and drew me closer, as if his embrace could fix what Dr. Kaminski couldn't. "Whatever happens," he said, "we'll get through this."

"How do you know that?" I asked.

"Because I know us," he replied, wiping my tears away.

I didn't ask him how we were supposed to face a future filled with harsher and harsher treatments as I slowly marched toward death. Instead, I pulled myself together and assured Alex I was fine. In fact, I told him I was going to stop at one of our favorite antique stores and then head home to start dinner.

I did stop at the antique store. I usually loved rummaging for bargains, but on that day, I wandered through all three floors of the store without ever noticing a single item. All I could think about was lymphoma. Cancer. Chemotherapy. Clinical trials. Alex. Juli. What would happen to our life?

I told myself that test results can be skewed. Surely there was an acceptable arbitrary margin of error. Had Dr. Kaminski confused me with someone else? It was much too soon to surrender to scientific "facts," I thought. Yep, I was a hard sell grasping at straws. But having an incurable disease takes some getting used to.

Alex, on the other hand, would tell me many months later that he promptly hunkered down for a long haul. He immediately refused to indulge in what-ifs, and he saw the futility of expending energy on wishing that cancer hadn't dropped into our life. It had, and so he consciously asked himself what he could do to mitigate the disruption. Knowing that he would be of no help to me if he allowed himself to crumble, he resolved to stay focused on a positive outcome and to safeguard our optimistic attitudes, which he believed were absolutely critical to the ultimate goal of wellness. He saw that we would be spending more and more time at the hospital and that managing his time would be more crucial than ever. He promised himself he would assume my job when necessary and learn how to juggle between medical appointments, work and whatever else it would take to help me heal. Deliberately, he appointed himself Head Cheerleader, although it would take me months to notice.

I had promised to call Juli after our appointment. By the time I had wandered through the antique store, I'd pulled myself together enough to call her. Sitting in my car in the parking lot, I dialed her number and hoped that I could sound strong and brave. I think, I hope, that I did. I told her there were several clinical trials I could enter, that there was great hope for a cure and that, yes, this was one big royal pain, but I would be fine. I tried to sound as hopeful and cheerful as I possibly could. All I really wanted was to collapse in her arms and tell her how much I loved her, but she was 1200 miles away.

Next, I stopped by the office. Alex wasn't expecting me, and I found him sitting at my desk wearing a mask of fear on his face, clearly visible for the first time, at least to me. Greta, his 18-year-old daughter, sat across from him, weeping. She rose, walked the few steps toward me, and put her arms around me. I assured her things would be fine, that this was a just a little bump in the road of life. Somehow I managed to keep my composure, although the look I had seen on Alex's face nearly shattered it.

At dinner that evening, we told Zan, Alex's 13-year-old son who lived with us most of the time. Although Alex and I had not discussed in any great detail how we would handle a major illness, we had both agreed to maintain as normal a life as possible. We briefly explained what was happening to Zan and assured him that we would not allow this to affect his normal routine. Thirteen-year-old boys have much better things to think about than their wicked stepmother's problems, and Zan took the news in stride. Like his father, he never turns a problem into a crisis.

When I told my sister Karen, I wanted to keep the conversation as light as possible in order to alleviate her fears. Humor, I believe, allows us to avoid staring directly at adversity and I had always used it to masquerade my own fears. Wisecracks had, in fact, often kept me from falling to pieces.

My sisters Nancy and Karen were sixteen and thirteen respectively when I was born, the result, I suspect, of an amorous accident. Both Karen and Nancy, who had died eleven years earlier, had wellendowed, voluptuous bodies. I have always been flat, straight and skinny, and always, they teased me unmercifully. It was time to get Karen back.

I excitedly told her that I'd seen the reports with my own eyes and that all the radiologists, pathologists and doctors had referred to my swollen lymph nodes as breasts, not chest. Medical science had finally proven that I do indeed have them, however underdeveloped. Karen giggled as I had wanted her to, and it set the tone for the truth.

I lay awake in the darkness much of that night listening to Alex's quiet, steady breathing, and I grieved for him. He hadn't bargained for this. And I reminisced about falling in love. Initially, our romance had been complicated by the distance between us as well as by the scars from our previous marriages. But eventually we'd become the best of friends because, I thought, we simply balanced and completed each other.

I'd often laughed that we should be the poster couple for Opposites Attract. He's serious. I'm playful. He's a conversational minimalist, saying in two words what it would take me twenty sentences to say. While he withholds his thoughts and feelings, I easily divulge what is on my mind, at least to a few people. I'm the romantic while he's the pragmatist. He's a workaholic while — well, let's just say that I work hard when I work but I also like to play. While my emotions rise high and fall low, he remains calm through anything and everything. Sometimes I'd teased him, "You alive under all that composure?"

I worried that Alex was much too stoic to cope with a major illness and was afraid that he would have no idea how to reach out for help. Not only that, he'd never endured the day-to-day agonies of illness. Up until then, he and his small family had been blessed with excellent health. His mother Lisa, at eighty-three, and his father Ted, at eighty-nine, still lived in their own home not far from ours, walked five miles a day, drove themselves wherever they wanted to go, wintered in Florida, and suffered not a single ailment. He couldn't have a clue what to expect.

On the other hand, I knew from experience that a major illness wreaks havoc on families because I grew up surrounded by it. When I was six, my mother's mother became blind and bedridden. Since she was a Christian Scientist, we never knew exactly why. As a child, I knew only that my mother spent her days in my grandmother's room caring for her. When I was twelve, my father's mother became bedridden and moved in with us. My mother could not manage the care of both grandmothers, so my parents hired a live-in nurse to help. She hated kids. I hated her back.

For almost as far back as I could remember until almost the time I left for college, illness had dictated every move our family had made, and I had vowed that when I grew up, I would never, ever let illness dominate the life of my family. Would that soon change? I cringed at the thought.

Lying in bed that night, I thought, too, about losing someone you love. Alex hadn't faced that experience, but years earlier I had lost my father and my sister. I recalled Daddy's illness, a stroke which had immobilized his body and nearly destroyed his speech. At the time, I was a grown woman who loved her father dearly, but those old childhood scars had resurfaced and I had hated being around illness again, especially illness that claimed someone for whom I cared so deeply.

I did, however, recognize the indignities that Daddy suffered during the year between his stroke and his death. His sharp lawyer's mind was trapped in a broken shell, and though he never surrendered his sense of humor, he despised his helplessness. That I understood, and I had secretly hoped that I would just drop dead one day. I doubted that cancer would give me that luxury.

I wondered how Alex or Juli would feel if they had to watch me waste away as I had watched Daddy. Far away and entrenched with her own family and job, Juli at least would be spared the daily agonies. But how would Alex cope? Would they feel as helpless as I did when I had wanted to fix Daddy and had driven myself half crazy when I couldn't? Neither Alex nor Juli had probably ever considered the fact that I would not always be around, and I wondered how much they depended on me, and for what. Until Daddy's illness, I had never realized how much I had depended on him for a million little things, and I still missed our lively conversations. Would Alex and Juli miss talking with me as much as I still missed talking with Daddy?

I thought, too, of my sister Nancy. She was fifty-nine and perfectly healthy when she got up one morning, had a stroke and was comatose by lunch. In the hospital, my beautiful, glamorous sister was nearly indistinguishable from the sheets. Honoring a decision she had made much earlier, my brother-in-law and nephews stopped life support the day after her stroke. Moments later, she died as I held her hand, and I ached with sadness when I walked away down the long hospital corridor. That was one walk I fervently hoped Alex and Juli would never have to make, but hope and my body were clearly out of synch, the latter obviously not caring for them in the least.

I have never reconciled whether prolonged illness or sudden death is easier to bear. Selfishly, I was glad for the extra year with my father after his stroke, but it was painfully hard on him. And knowing his death was imminent made it no easier to bear when it came. What I did know was that illness and death were stressful and sad and time-consuming. Alex didn't. How could I possibly explain to him that he was in for an emotional roller coaster ride? I finally fell asleep that night promising myself to talk with him about this.

The following morning, I begged Alex not to try to carry the burden alone. This was not the time for his disciplined stoicism. Stress, I reminded him, can damage our bodies, and he was already on stress overload without this challenge. I told him that I was afraid his health was as much at risk as mine if he were to internalize his feelings about my illness as much as he did about everything else. I pleaded with him not to let me and cancer harm him, and I suggested that he somehow learn to express his emotions to me or to anyone who would listen. Since he said little as I spoke, I virtually delivered a monologue. Was he listening, I wondered?

I forgot to tell Alex that I wasn't ready to reveal our misfortune to anyone outside of our family. Though I was always one to tackle life's challenges head on, I didn't yet know how to respond to other people, and I wasn't ready to hear, "Oh you poor thing." Not only that, I couldn't wrap my head around what was unfolding. Such an insidious disease couldn't possibly — wouldn't dare — interrupt our life. When I spoke or thought of lymphoma, it was as if I were thinking or speaking of someone else. And surely other facts would surface that would disprove the findings and deliver me from it. Yes, I wore a cloak of delusion, and it fit quite nicely, thank you very much.

Although I had encouraged Alex to express his emotions, he's ordinarily such a private person that I guess I never thought he would say much to anyone, but within days after my speech, the arrival of flowers was evidence that he had heeded my advice and divulged our predicament. Although caught by surprise, I thought it was healthy for him to open up and was relieved that he was verbalizing his feelings. It never occurred to me that Alex — being Alex — was hardly verbalizing his feelings or looking for support. He was searching for specific answers from anyone who had faced the disease. He wanted to know what they had done — and where.

Within days of launching his fact-finding mission, we had more flowers than I knew what to do with. Of course I appreciated the sentiments from each and every sender, and I was deeply touched by the outpouring of good wishes from everyone who knew nothing else to do, but at the risk of sounding ungrateful, I was also desperately holding on to any semblance of normalcy. And our house normally didn't resemble a morgue.

Worse, I couldn't bear to watch the flowers shrivel and die. Each death reminded me of the brevity of life, and I feared that I, too, might suffer the same fate. After about a week of receiving bouquets, I gave away subsequent arrivals to avoid witnessing their speedy demise. One friend sent a plant — at last something immortal — and I carefully nurtured it throughout my illness. However distorted, cancer gave new perspective to the simplest of gestures.

Alex, too, began to veer away from normalcy. Dragging him out on weeknights was about as easy as extracting teeth from a live alligator. He was too busy reviewing paperwork from the office. Every night. And he'd never been able to pull off a surprise. But early in February, when he told me not to plan anything for a particular Tuesday evening, he delighted me with dinner at a charming restaurant followed by a performance of "Phantom of the Opera."

Soon after, on another weeknight, we enjoyed The St. Petersburg Symphony Orchestra, which played some of my favorite music. I couldn't help but close my eyes and wonder if we'd ever see that beautiful city. We'd certainly hoped to — someday.

Everyone else seemed to be taking this far more seriously than I, perhaps because I knew so little about lymphoma. Or perhaps because I had wrapped myself in that cloak of delusion — or at least denial.

By the end of February, when our home looked and smelled like a morgue and Dr. Kaminski was certain of lymphoma, I wanted to argue with the entire medical community that the test results were wrong. My body was telling me a different story than what the reports were telling them. I could stay awake almost every day, my feet felt fine, and the hot flashes were dormant. As far as I was concerned, I felt just fine. Never mind that I had forgotten what fine really felt like.

And how in the world would I find time to accomplish everything I needed to accomplish if I had to continue going to the hospital all the time? My day planner had no room for any internal malfunction. Maybe if I just kept busy, it would all go away. Call me the Queen of Denial.

Oh, I'd wept briefly a couple of times, mainly out of frustration, but I couldn't bring myself to believe that I was staring a life threatening disease squarely in the face. I mostly joked about it. Alex and I had few conversations about lymphoma, and those were not only brief but also limited mostly to the schedule of appointments. Besides the one monologue I had delivered encouraging him to express his emotions, we had avoided serious discussions — which was exactly the way I wanted it. I never did take my own advice very well.

● ● ●

I have heard there are troubles of more than one kind.
Some come from ahead and some come from behind.
But I've bought a big bat. I'm all ready you see.
Now my troubles are going to have troubles with me!
— Dr. Seuss

5. | BIG GIRLS *DO* CRY — AND THEN THEY GET TO WORK

One afternoon in late February I was on my way home from a meeting with clients when the word "cancer" screamed from a news program on the radio, to which I had not been paying particular attention. How dare that radio remind of cancer? Annoyed, I changed the station, only to hear the song "Big Girls Don't Cry." Wrong. Big girls do cry. Suddenly, a torrent of tears gushed forth so hard that I couldn't see to drive. I pulled into a cul-de-sac, stopped my car, and let it all out. I sobbed so hard that my whole body shook like a tree in a hurricane. I pounded the steering wheel until my hands hurt. I screamed and cursed and cried out, "Please let me live. Please. Please. Please."

A thousand thoughts that I had been repressing hurled me into a tempest of raw fear, frustration, confusion, grief and anger. Would I live to dance at my grandchildren's weddings? Would I live to see them graduate from college? Would I even live to see them start kindergarten? Would I grow old with Alex? I'd counted on many years together, and I grieved at the possible loss of anything less than a long lifetime with him.

And what had I ever done that really mattered? At least Alex's homes were standing testimony to a lifetime of work, but what would I leave behind? Who would keep the marketing materials I had written? Who would remember the countless hours I had spent helping clients choose a floorplan, a kitchen sink, a bathroom tile?

Would I become deformed and emaciated? How much pain would there be? Would I become bedridden like my grandmothers? I couldn't bear the thought. If I couldn't enjoy life, contribute to it, and remain independent, I didn't want to stick around.

But I *did* want to stick around. And how was I supposed to confront this predicament? After what seemed like hours but was probably minutes, my body quit heaving and the torrent of tears slowed to a trickle. I could just see my father reminding me, "When the going gets tough, the tough get going," and I tried to persuade myself that cancer was tough, but I was tougher. Silently at first, then out loud, I began to chant, "I can beat this. I can beat this. I can beat this."

There in the car, I had a long talk with myself about the power of positive thinking and the strength of the human spirit. "Mind over matter," my Christian Scientist grandmother had preached. "Never give up," said Winston Churchill. And when I remembered that the best defense is a good offense, I knew what I had to do. I would take the offensive, defy the odds, the probabilities and the medians — and I would live. By the time I finally headed home, I had fiercely and passionately resolved to tackle whatever was necessary to take the offense.

That was easier said than done. A huge part of offensive strategy is knowing your opponent, which meant that I had to learn about lymphoma. I'd spent my adult life helping people buy and plan their new homes and there's nothing scientific about that. In fact, I must have been born with two right brains because I'd happily breezed through life with imagination on steroids and science on ignore, but that left me up the creek when cancer called. The most I knew about cells was that mine was usually in the bottom of my purse when it rang. Proteins? Lots of them in a good steak. And forget about DNA and lymphocytes.

How was I to learn everything I needed to know? At least I had the presence of mind to realize that Dr. Kaminski's and Judy's role was to treat my disease, not to be my personal Lymphoma 101 tutors. Instead, I designated Alex as my science expert. He has both sides of his brain, and he uses them. Whether it's physics or history, music or economics, he has a natural curiosity for all living and non-living subjects. Best of all, he graduated pre-med! Surely he would have no trouble understanding the disease, its causes and cures, and explaining it all to me.

What was I thinking? Alex definitely has his good points, but he explains almost everything on a post-doctorate level using very few words. Clearly, he was not the person to ask for simple explanations, but I did. As questions came to mind over the next few days, I fired them off faster than a machine gun. Alex, what's a cell? Alex, explain DNA. Alex, I thought protein was something you ate. Alex, what's a lymphocyte? Alex, explain the lymph system. Alex, Alex, Alex…. I drove him crazy with questions.

I begged him to answer each one as if he were talking to a five-year-old. Draw me a picture. Use simple words and analogies. He would try. I would then ask a question in response to his explanation. He'd try again. I'd ask another question. Soon he was off somewhere in left field as far as I was concerned. His unfathomable answers were making my brain feel feeble. Worse, my education was at a standstill.

I'd been calling Alex whenever and wherever questions popped into my mind. In the kitchen. On the way to a meeting. When he was standing in the middle of a construction site with saws and nail-guns drowning out my voice. I suggested that we could accomplish much more if we just sat down quietly one evening. Alex agreed, so I made questions and notes, and I covered the dining room table with booklets and pamphlets that we had gathered. I even brought out encyclopedias. Remember them — before Google?

I wanted Alex to start by explaining a cell and how it functions. He began. I wasn't getting it, so I began to draw what I thought he was saying. No, that wasn't right, he'd say. Well, draw it for me, I'd reply. Alex isn't an artist. We kept going. I still didn't quite grasp the cell concept, but I went on to DNA, knowing that lymphoma had something to do with a flaw in the DNA.

Alex, could you explain just what DNA is? "It's deoxyribonucleic acid," he answered. Like that told me a lot.

"And just what does it do?" I asked.

"It chemically writes each person's genetic program," he answered, as if I were supposed to understand that little tidbit of information.

"And just what does that mean and what does it have to do with lymphoma?" I questioned.

Alex is normally unflappable, but he flapped. One of his eyebrows cocked, his jaw squared, his voice dropped, he looked straight at me and said, "Betsy, you're not asking for a crash course. You're trying to go to graduate school without the basics." Then he rose from the chair and took a couple of steps toward the kitchen before turning around and adding, "Scientists were just figuring out the significance of DNA when I was in college, and that was more than thirty years ago." And then he walked out of the room.

I had pushed Alex to his limit. Hadn't I always known that if I wanted a simple answer, Alex was not the person from whom to get it? Worse, not only had our conversation exposed the inadequacy of his teaching skills, but maybe, just maybe, he was having difficulty adjusting to the idea of his wife having cancer. Maybe he thought I was the stupidest person alive. I felt horrible. To the very best of his ability, he really had tried.

That night I sat studying at the dining room table long after Alex went to bed. Until then, I had whined that all the pamphlets we'd gathered were useless because they only contained incomprehensible words and concepts. I'd even complained that their names were threatening. "What You Need to Know About Non-Hodgkin's Lymphoma" should have been called "What Someone Else Needs to Know About Non-Hodgkin's Lymphoma." "Chemotherapy and

You" should have been entitled "Chemotherapy and Some Other Poor Soul." But that night, I opened my mind and read every booklet and article. I even drew circles to represent cells and wrote their different parts in the circles. My drawings looked like a five-year-old's, but they were the visual aids that I needed to help me understand and remember what I was learning.

Still, lymphoma — like all cancers — is a very difficult disease to understand, especially lacking some scientific background. Each patient's disease presents itself and behaves differently. There are indolent and aggressive forms and several sub-categories of those. Mine was of the indolent nature, which to me simply meant that it was too slow or too lazy to kill me immediately. It was also circulating in my bloodstream, and even with my limited knowledge, I knew that blood circulated to every organ and tissue. By the time I finally went to bed, I couldn't help but wonder if I was just one big blob of cancer. But I also could hardly wait to recite all the details of my new knowledge to Alex.

The following morning, we stood in the kitchen and I proudly showed him my pictures. With my hands on my hips and a sheepish grin on my face, I pranced around the kitchen island rapidly rattling off every bit of information I could remember. Talking about anything scientific was so out of character for me, and he tried not to laugh, but his amusement was quite apparent. I told him not to worry about understanding the more recent DNA discoveries. As the new science expert of the household, I'd catch up on them and fill him in. Sure, he chuckled, as he put his arms around me.

We had less than two weeks before our next visit with Dr. Kaminski, and I felt like a college kid facing the biggest exam of my life. I scoured the Internet and found it strewn with cancer sites, but the information I found was so frightening that I was convinced I was going to die next week, if not sooner. After gasping several times, I somehow had the wits to realize that I had no idea how to judge the veracity of the material or the relevance it may or may not have to me. I got off the Internet and voraciously re-read pamphlets and articles that came from reliable sources. And little by little, I began to comprehend more. It's amazing what you can learn when your life is on the line.

Alex also became much better at answering questions. Or had I just become better at listening? It was probably a combination of both. Months later, he would tell me that he had genuinely wanted to answer my questions, but had initially been frustrated by my foolish attempts to learn in two weeks that which I had ignored for a lifetime. And since he was only beginning to learn about lymphoma, he couldn't possibly be the expert he thought I expected him to be. He had also begun to comprehend the severity of the disease, suspected that I didn't, and feared that any explanation he might give could possibly lower my spirits — which he still saw as positive, despite my unrealistic expectation of becoming an expert scientist overnight.

Part of me wanted to maintain a normal work schedule, but I quickly began to resent interruptions. When I met with one of our clients to help them choose paint colors, my own impatience surprised even me. I had always enjoyed every phase of helping families plan and build their homes, but my patience turned to agitation after they agonized over a couple of shades of off-white — for two hours! Didn't they know that they were keeping me from something far more important than their stupid paint? Not only that, I wanted to scream, "It won't matter two months from now. Go home and spend time with your kids and leave me to my studies." Yes, indeed, I had work to do to save my own neck.

● ● ●

You cannot do everything at once, so find people you trust to help you.
And don't be afraid to say no.
– Jane Seymour

6. | IN DOCTOR WE TRUST

I n January, after I was diagnosed with lymphoma, I retrieved a
copy of the blood test that the gynecologist had ordered a year
and a half earlier, and there — in bold print — was my lymphocyte count. High, it said, in big, bold letters. I stared at the paper for
a very long time, feeling betrayed by a female gynecologist who —
if she had bothered to read the report — might not have blown me
off as another casualty of middle-aged menopause. And I shuddered
to think what might have happened if my cancer had been one of
the fast-growing kinds.

It's no wonder that Dr. Kaminski had to earn my trust. It's not
that I didn't want to trust him. I did, but I desperately needed
answers to questions I never dared to ask, except in my journal as
follows:

Dear Doc,

Here we are, you and me, our lives connected by cancer. My cancer. Under the circumstances, I'm really glad to
have you in my life, and I want our relationship to be very,
very long and very, very good, but since I can't find a manual on how to build our relationship, I'm guessing that, like

any good one, it has to start with trust. But trust takes time, which we don't have, so I have some things to ask and say.

First, just what am I trusting in you? That you're brilliant, cool under pressure, experienced, knowledgeable and up to date on the latest miracles of modern science for my type of cancer? That you won't be too proud to call in colleagues, or send me to them, if you get stumped or run out of ideas? That you'll always be honest with me no matter how hard it is for you or me? That you'll help me set realistic expectations without ever stealing my hope? That you'll be my strength if I'm too weak to be strong? That you won't give up on me if the going gets rough and it looks like I won't be one of your success stories?

Do you have any idea that it's hard enough to put my trust in you but even harder to put blind faith in the people I can't see but on whom you rely? Like the pathologists who look at tiny pieces of me or the radiologists who interpret pictures of my innards. You may know their credentials, but I don't, and how do I know that they're in a good mood when they decide my future?

I get that you went to medical school to learn how to identify and treat disease, not to listen to me blather on about how cancer is more than a physical problem. That it's really personal. That it sweeps us patients and our families into a tempest of confusion, fear, frustration, vulnerability and isolation from the healthy world. I'll try very hard to check those emotions at the door when you and I visit, but if they creep into the examining room, is it too much to ask you to recognize that I'm not just a collection of cells that need to be fixed while you also work to fix my wayward cells?

And Doc, surely you know that your sophisticated equipment can't see the parts of me that make me who I am. And I am not my cancer. No machine can identify the parts that make me love and laugh. And none can calculate how very afraid I am. Of what lies ahead. Of pain. Of medical procedures. Of becoming a number in a bureaucracy where no one will care whether I end up running a marathon or being turned over in a bed like a piece of meat on a rotisserie. And of dying. Could you occasionally share my fear and shore up my hope?

Doc, I've tried to put myself in your shoes, but I can't imagine how, day in and day out, you see humanity at its weakest and still find the strength to help us patients. I'm just glad that you can. And I know that I need much more from you than you need from me, but I'll do anything to help you help me, if only you can squeeze out a little time to teach me how to be a good cancer patient in addition to everything else that I ask of you.

Neither you nor I can predict the future, Doc, and I don't expect you to do more than is humanly and medically possible. But may I trust you to treat my future as if it were your very own?

● ● ●

Of course I never asked Dr. Kaminski those questions. I never had to. His actions spoke far more convincingly than any words he might have spoken. From the moment we met, he and Judy seemed to care about my cancer *and* about the rest of me. Early on, they nearly dispelled my fear of an impersonal health care system by taking the time to learn my name, not just my patient number, and by patiently answering all our questions — which I tried to limit to a reasonable number — without ever making us feel dumb for not knowing the answers. They had even answered questions we had not known to ask.

They also gave me copies of every report from every test I had. Even though I didn't have a clue what most of the words meant, the message was clear: we have nothing to hide from you, and we want you to be informed about your disease. What a concept, I thought. Not only did they give me copies, but Judy and Dr. Kaminski referred to reports when they relayed results from tests. That meant that they were actually reading the reports. Better yet, they always reported test results quickly, as if knowing that I would otherwise sit home and stew. It was amazing, I thought, that they seemed to know the importance of trust as much as I did.

Despite our rising comfort level with Dr. Kaminski, Alex and I still hoped that his diagnosis was wrong. At least I still hoped. Alex would later tell me that he had almost given up all hope for an incorrect diagnosis and had begun to worry about the possibility of human error as I progressed through treatment. Wrong medications or incorrect interpretations could spell big trouble.

Alex and I talked about getting a second opinion. It's not that we doubted the competency of Dr. Kaminski or his team. Our only desire — at least my only desire — for a second opinion stemmed from the hope that I could find one to refute the diagnosis so that our life could return to normal. And normal was all either one of us wanted. Too bad my mischievous cells had other plans for us.

We weren't sure where to head for a second opinion since we knew that people go to U of M to get them. "But," said Alex, "we'll do whatever we have to do. Check it out."

Before I could check anything out, a friend in another state asked if she could show my biopsy report to the pathologist at the hospital where she worked. Alex and I thought that would be an easy way to obtain a second opinion, so I faxed the report to her. Within hours, my friend sent a fax from her pathologist stating that "no significant lymphoma" was circulating in my bloodstream. Excuse me, but what lymphoma is not significant?

Had we misunderstood Dr. Kaminski? He had said that lymphoma was circulating in my bloodstream, hadn't he? I sent Judy an email and she quickly confirmed what we thought we had heard.

Alex and I were not only confused but very concerned over these two differing opinions, and we wrestled with whom to believe.

We scoured the Internet and called the National Cancer Institute and the American Cancer Society, hoping to find the best lymphoma specialist in the country, and we did find a handful of doctors who are considered among the world's leading experts in lymphoma. Dr. Kaminski was right there among them, and I was already under his care — and in our own backyard, no less. We also learned that people from all over the world travel to Ann Arbor for second opinions and that U of M was one of a small number of elite hospitals designated by the National Cancer Institute (NCI) as a Comprehensive Cancer Center.

NCI designated centers are recognized for their scientific excellence and must meet stringent criteria in order to receive NCI's designation. Not only are they hotbeds of research, but they are generally where patients find the latest and greatest advances.

Alex and I quickly realized how lucky we were that I had landed in Dr. Kaminski's care, and we concluded that we would place our trust in him and his colleagues. It helped that we had just learned about the team approach at the clinic. Until then, we had not realized that other doctors reviewed my case with Dr. Kaminski. Nor had we realized that the clinic's pathologists specialize in conditions of the blood. Meeting each week, this team of specialists *was* my second opinion. In fact, there were twenty or so opinions in those meetings. It seemed not only logical to trust the people who study lymphoma — and only lymphoma — on a daily basis, but it also gave us a tremendous level of comfort.

It also seemed that Dr. Kaminski was not only an expert in lymphoma, but he and his colleagues were beginning to convince me that they were experts in protecting the human spirit. He and Judy had tried to assure us that many people can live normal lives with lymphoma, and they had warned us that fear diminishes the quality of life for others. They had encouraged us to live our normal life and to think of myself as well while they worked to increase the length and quality of mine. Intuitively knowing that we were wrestling with uncertainties, they offered assurances and cheerfulness in generous proportions, and because they were treating me as a real human being, it seemed only fair to extend the same courtesy.

But how? I sensed that we had a long relationship ahead of us — at least I hoped it would be long — and I suspected that it would be unlike any other I had ever had. And what did I know about a patient/physician relationship?

To begin with, it seemed that my expectations should be realistic. Years of observing people in our own business had taught me that the clients who worked with us through the building process had a much easier and happier experience than the ones who placed impossible demands on us. I recalled a client some years back who had wanted us to remove a structural column in the basement in order to accommodate his furniture arrangement. Never mind that its placement had been carefully engineered to support the first and second floors or that the building inspectors would never have approved the structure had we done so. The buyer refused to accept the necessity of that column, much less the ramifications of its removal, and neither his money nor his whining could make us remove it.

Yes, experience told me that I'd be a whole lot happier in my unhappy situation if I worked *with* Dr. Kaminski. Still unsure exactly how, at least I figured out that I would set myself up for disappointment if I placed unrealistic expectations on him. Even the best doctors can't always put scrambled eggs back in the shell, but I was growing confident that Dr. Kaminski would do his best and that he and his team would treat my future as if it were their very own.

● ● ●

Everything starts with yourself — with you making up
your mind about what you're going to do.
— *Tony Dorsett*

7. | PICKING MY POISON

By the time Alex and I met with Dr. Kaminski and Judy on March 11, I had succeeded in putting a tremendous amount of pressure on myself, but had failed to cram medical school into two weeks. Still, I'd learned enough to think that I was ready to hear whatever Dr. Kaminski had to say. I wasn't.

It was time, he said, to begin treatment. I'd known that my counts were rising because Judy had been faithfully reporting the results of the blood tests since we'd last met. But hold on, Dr. Kaminski, I just figured out what a cell is. Let's not get ahead of me. With his usual patience and diplomacy, he recited our options and asked what we wanted to do. What did we want to do? How about rewinding life and starting the year over without lymphoma? And how was I supposed to choose one of the options? I hadn't finished cellular biology, much less medical school.

Dr. Kaminski again explained the choices and repeated that it was best to start with the lighter drugs and work up to the stronger ones. Wow — that was certainly something to look forward to. I wanted to be glad to have options, but I recoiled at the thought of every one of them. But then again, cremation was even less appealing.

I'll be forever grateful to Dr. Kaminski for the patience with which he repeated the risks and benefits of each of the various treatments. I listened as carefully as I could while my mind raced through all the possibilities, but I was unable to make a decision that would affect my very life when I knew so very little. I turned to Alex to make it for me, but it was obvious that he was as confused and overwhelmed as I. What, Alex and I asked, would Dr. Kaminski suggest if I were his wife or daughter?

Dr. Kaminski recommended a clinical trial during which a chemotherapy called CVP would be administered eight times, once every three weeks. If I stayed in remission for six months after the chemotherapy, I would have a two to one chance of receiving a vaccine to fight the cancer.

CVP — an acronym for cyclophosphamide, vincristene and prednisone — is one of the lighter combinations often used as the first treatment for my type of lymphoma. The benefit was obvious: it would hopefully grant me a stay of execution, although for how long was anybody's guess. The risks? I'd checked out these drugs and learned that cyclophosphamide is a derivative of mustard gas, which is used in chemical warfare. And vincristine is a derivative of the Madagascar periwinkle, which grows in Florida and as everyone there knows, is poisonous if ingested — not that I had ever intended to eat it.

No wonder the list of side effects seemed endless. This combination of drugs could imperil my veins, my heart, my liver, my lungs and just about every other organ in my body. A partial list of collateral damage could include mouth sores, hair loss, fatigue, insomnia, weight gain, weight loss, gastric ulcers, diabetes, cataracts, glaucoma, high blood pressure, blood clots, constipation, diarrhea, seizures, rapid mood changes from euphoria to depression, and occasionally, psychosis.

See the problem? Even the drugs can't make up their minds whether to cause diarrhea or constipation, insomnia or fatigue, weight gain or weight loss, euphoria or depression. And, in exchange for one affliction, I could end up with several — and this was Chemo Lite! Who wouldn't be psychotic? I thought about asking Dr. Kaminski if he'd really taken that "First Do No Harm" oath. It's no wonder that I tried to buy time. Although Alex and I had read about various treatments and trials during the previous weeks, I wasn't ready to commit, not only because chemo terrified me, but also because I didn't feel competent to make the most important decision I had ever made in my life. I think I wanted Alex to make it for me, but he was no more capable than I. We asked Dr. Kaminski if we could let him know by Thursday. It was Monday. He agreed.

We had scheduled meetings with clients on Monday and Tuesday nights. Just as Alex and I began reviewing our options on Wednesday night, Zan walked into the room and announced that he needed to get some schoolwork he had left at his mother's house. She had company and couldn't possibly bring it to him. Stunned, I thought, "She has what? We're trying to figure out how to save my life." Alex drove Zan to retrieve his papers while I sat home and fumed. Balancing a normal life with major decisions and medical treatment was going to require some effort.

Alex returned within a half hour and let me whine for a few minutes about having to choose something I didn't want in the first place, but life hands us all difficult choices that have to be made and we got down to the business of making it. We re-read information about the clinical trial as well as about the other treatments Dr. Kaminski had explained. We weighed the risks and benefits of each, and eventually concluded that the trial offered an option that I wouldn't otherwise have. And I needed all the options I could get. Not only that, the vaccine offered the most promise and hope of anything else that was available. And if I were in the group that didn't get it, nothing would be lost since CVP would have been my initial treatment anyway.

On Friday, we met with one of Dr. Kaminski's colleagues, Dr. Andrej Jakubowiak, to learn more about the trial. I still wanted to know as much about lymphoma as the doctors knew, and I was frantically holding on to a faint hope that they were wrong. On the way to our appointment, I meekly asked Alex if he thought there was any possibility of a mistake. My heart sank as he answered that he thought the chances were slim.

In the examining room, Marian Blaesser, Dr. Jakubowiak's nurse practitioner, examined me. Much to my surprise, she had hardly entered the room when Alex asked what were the chances that all these test results were wrong. Marian must have heard that question before because she patiently explained the odds. None. Too many tests had confirmed the same thing. Alex had tried, and I loved him for his effort.

Marian sensed my frustration about not fully understanding lymphoma. She answered several questions until Dr. Jakubowiak arrived, and he answered many more. Still, it wasn't enough. Recognizing my apprehension, Marian told me the same thing that Dr. Kaminski and Judy had tried to tell me, but which I had not heard. She simply stated, "Betsy, it takes many years to learn about lymphoma, and even then, we don't always understand everything about it. The best thing you can do is let us understand it for you while you keep yourself strong."

In the frenzy I'd been in, it would have been easy to take Marian's comment as condescending, but the compassion in her voice told me she was sincerely trying to help me. At that moment, I realized that cancer wasn't going to wait for me to go to medical school and that I had a whole team of some of the best doctors in the country who knew more about lymphoma than I would ever know. Then and there, I decided to make the most of their experience and expertise and to do everything within my power to help them help me, which is, after all, what I wanted. To me, that meant learning enough about the disease to understand questions and answer them thoroughly. It meant understanding enough to know when to report changes between appointments. It meant following instructions. And it meant keeping myself otherwise as healthy and positive as I could. Yes sirree, I might not know a lot about lymphoma, but I was going to be a conscientious, coachable patient.

With decisions made, a weight lifted off my shoulders. I signed the necessary papers for the clinical trial. Another CT scan and a bone marrow biopsy would be necessary in order for me to qualify for the trial. Qualify? Couldn't I try out for something more fun and less painful?

Throughout the appointment, Alex sat in the chair while I sat on the examining table. His normal poker face had remained in the parking lot that morning. There was that mask of fear I had seen once before, and it tore at my heart. As Marian and I went to the front desk to make the necessary appointments, my eyes filled with tears for Alex. I'll never forget Marian putting her arm around my shoulder, trying to comfort me. "I've never met that man before today. He's in such pain," she said.

"I know, and I don't know how to make him feel better," I lamented. Alex would later tell me that he saw, crystal clearly, that the only certainty along the road ahead was uncertainty. He hated the thought of my undergoing chemotherapy. And he was just beginning to grasp that Head Cheerleader was going to be a very difficult role.

● ● ●

There isn't a person anywhere who isn't capable of
doing more than he thinks he can.
— *Henry Ford*

8. | COWARDS GET CANCER TOO

I'm sure that my maiden name — Kurka — predisposed me to cowardice. In Polish, "kurka" means "little chicken," and the only more appropriate name would have been whatever word means "big chicken," which is what I had always been when it came to needles, the sight of blood or any other medical procedure. So far I had somehow managed to tolerate all the tests with unusual aplomb, but I really dreaded the bone marrow biopsy. And I had the whole weekend to fret about it.

A needle, 3/16" in diameter — almost a quarter of an inch! — would be inserted through my hip bone and a syringe would draw out my marrow. It sounded more like a jackhammer tearing through my bone, followed by Roto Rooter sucking out sludge through a hose. Yikes!

When Juli and I spoke on Saturday, she asked if I had been told what to expect. Yes, and I was less than thrilled. Did they tell you they would medicate you? No, I was to be awake. "Mom, you really don't want to do that," she said. No kidding. A nurse herself, Juli suggested, "We give our patients a drug called Versed. They're awake but remember nothing," she said. "Don't be afraid to ask for that or something like it. You may have to have another bone marrow biopsy sometime and it will be much easier if you don't dread it." That sounded like a great idea to me.

Fully aware of my aversion to needles and such, Juli asked if anyone had mentioned a port. No, no one had mentioned a port, but I'd read a little about them. Juli further explained that since cancer patients require frequent blood draws and chemotherapy can make the veins tired and tender, ports were sometimes surgically placed beneath the skin through which all needles for blood draws and infusions could be inserted. Disgusting. I couldn't imagine looking at something like that, much less feeling it.

Juli then said that I had one good thing going for me: great veins. "Thanks, Mom," she teased, "for the ugly hands you gave me. Our veins are everywhere, but in your case, they are going to be helpful, but you might want to ask your doctor what he thinks. A port might make your life a lot easier." I guess Dr. Kaminski thought I had great veins, too, because I never did get a port.

For the first time, I saw Juli's nursing skills in action, and I was very proud of her. My daughter, all grown up with babies of her own, was lending a caring hand to me when I needed it most. I was just beginning to grasp the vital role nurses play in patient care.

The big day for my clinical trial tryout came. Should I wear something special? Do my nails? Draw smiley faces on my hips? Early on, I had resolved to muster as much dignity as I possibly could during whatever procedures the doctors ordered. I didn't want anyone to know what a chicken I really was, and I certainly didn't want to whine too much to the people who were trying to help me. But I was convinced that I would suffer great pain that day, and I hoped that I could maintain a brave face.

Carolyn Shearer, the physician's assistant, came in to explain the procedure and how I would feel. It wouldn't take long, she assured me. Great, just a few minutes of agony and I could go home with my sore keister and painful memories. She could go home to whatever she went home to and sit comfortably. Lucky Carolyn. Poor me.

Dr. Craig Okada, Principal Investigator of the trial, arrived to draw the blood which would determine whether it was adequate to make the vaccine. Dr. Okada talked more about the trial and lymphoma, and then he asked Carolyn when I was going to get medicated. I wasn't, she answered, as I sat on the table with this jingle rattling in my head:

I'll lie upon my tummy. My back will face the ceiling.
Oh Good Lord, I'm really scared of what I'll soon be feeling.
I'll pull my pants down to my thighs. I'll moon all in the room
While Carolyn roots around my buns for marrow to exhume.
She said I'd feel some pressure. Has she ever had this done?
Is excruciating pain to be inflicted on each bun?
She'll probably don a hardhat, put jackhammer in her hand.
I hope I'll pass out quickly. Now wouldn't that be grand?
Bandaged up, she'll send me home with my sore derriere.
Oh, I pray with all my heart bad lymphocytes aren't there.

Dr. Okada became my new best friend that day. He thought it would be a good idea to give me some Versed so that I could be more comfortable during the procedure. There was some discussion about when I had last eaten, and the procedure would have to be postponed for two hours if I wanted Versed. Wanted it? Bring it on! I botched everyone's schedule that day, but I wanted to throw my arms around Dr. Okada's neck. Not only had he prescribed the drug, but he'd also spared me the embarrassment of begging for it! And the best news? I really don't remember anything about the procedure. Great stuff, that Versed.

Fearing that chemo would surely ground me, I flew, two days later, to Virginia to visit my mother and sister. For the past few years, Mother, at 92, had divided her time between our house and Karen's, but her congestive heart failure was worsening and she was traveling less frequently. Though her heart leaked like a sieve, she refused surgery to correct it. Doctors felt that her chances of surviving surgery were slim, anyway.

For the past five or six years, Mother had landed in the hospital two or three times each year. Her blood pressure would read 250-ish over 11 or 12, and the doctors would shake their heads in amazement that she survived these bouts, but she would always wake up with a smile and say, "Well, I'm still here." Still, I knew she would not live forever.

Karen and I had deliberated about whether to tell Mother what was happening to me. Her comprehension and memory had seemed to diminish in recent years, and we didn't want her to worry about losing another child. On the other hand, we agreed that we owed her a certain amount of honesty. We decided to tell her very briefly without actually saying "cancer," a word her generation considered a death sentence.

I gave considerable thought to how I would break the news to Mother. I knew that her optimistic nature would be helpful to all of us, and I smiled at the thought of her as a person, not just as my mother. She is one of the most gracious ladies you could ever hope to meet. She's a true Southern belle, the daughter of prim Victorian parents from whom she inherited her deep-seated beliefs of what is and isn't proper for young ladies, old ladies and every lady in between. Among other things, she taught me to wear white shoes only between Memorial Day and Labor Day, but only to wear white shoes if you positively could not find shoes to match your outfit. I'm sure I inherited a genetic predisposition for collecting shoes from her.

Growing up, I had judged my mother as a rigid product of an irrelevant era, but as an adult, I'd come to realize that she had raised me within the only frame of reference she knew, and I'd recognized how much I had learned from her, including the power to think positively. She had taught me, by example, that little acts of kindness could brighten the days of others. And what was the use of complaining? It only made those around you miserable. "Look around," she would say, "when you think you have no shoes. You'll always find someone else who has no feet."

During the first evening of my visit, I explained to Mother that I had a blood disorder. My white blood cells weren't dying after they divided, and too many cells could be harmful. Immediately she asked if having me late in her life had caused this. I felt so sorry that she might blame herself, and I assured her she had nothing to do with it. Doctors didn't know what caused it, but they could fix it. "How?" she wanted to know. They'd put me on some strong medicine over the course of about six months and I may not be able to travel to see her, but I would otherwise be fine.

Mother never asked if I had cancer or if the treatment I was describing was chemo. I'm not sure if she simply didn't want to know or didn't think to ask. She was, however, very concerned about me, and I joked that if my cells lived indefinitely, then surely so would I.

Our conversation was over almost as quickly as it had begun. Mother understood that I was sick, but it ended there. Mentally, she was too frail to sit through the details of some strange disease and too frail for me to lean on for strength. Or so I thought.

Still, I felt safe and peaceful sitting across from her at the dinner table. There in Virginia, lymphoma felt distant, as if it had stayed behind in Michigan. When my visit came to an end, it was hard to board the plane and return to the disease and the chemotherapy that was waiting for me. Much worse, I wondered what I would do if Mother went into the hospital — or died — and I was too sick to travel. As we said goodbye at the airport, I prayed it would not be our last.

I also desperately needed to see Juli and the babies, and I tried to squeeze in a quick trip to Florida, but schools were on spring break, and on the only days I could go, flights were overbooked with families and students who were heading for fun in the sun while I was heading straight for chemo. Lucky them. Frantic me. When would I see Juli and my grandchildren again?

Two weeks before starting chemo, I made the cut for the vaccine trial. I was absolutely positive that I would be selected to receive the vaccine, after which all would be fine and life could return to normal. Always realistic, Alex accepted the two to one odds better than I.

When not interrupted by various tests, I worked maniacally, afraid of when I might be able to work again. And I tried to psych myself up for chemo. Actually I tried to psych myself up for lots of vomiting.

Juli had sent me a book entitled *Getting Well Again* by O. Carl Simonton, Stephanie Matthews-Simonton and James L. Creighton. I had read it cover to cover and had begun to practice guided imagery that the book teaches. Self-training became a daily exercise, although it wasn't much different than what I had done for years. At work, for example, I'd never called it guided imagery, but I'd always envisioned writing a contract when I met with a prospective client. I simply learned to envision the cancer cells leaving my body instead of writing a contact. Of course, it takes more than a mind's image to eradicate cancer, but guided imagery became a tool that calmed me, made the treatments more bearable, and helped me to expect success.

I also decided to attend a lymphoma support group meeting — for all the wrong reasons. I went, not because I wanted support — oh no, I was much too strong and independent for that — but because I wanted to know what people there looked like and how ill or deformed the disease or medical procedures had made them. And my morbid curiosity outweighed my aversion to sitting around with a bunch of depressed people, tons of Kleenex boxes and social workers thanking me for sharing my feelings, all of which I was sure I would find.

Much to my surprise, nobody acted depressed. There was even some laughter. And I was a little embarrassed that perfect strangers saw right through my brave person mask. I guessed they'd all worn them, too. And much to my relief, everyone looked healthy and normal. Some had completed various treatments and had been in remission for some time. One had begun treatment recently. Others were still watching and waiting.

The woman who had recently begun treatment was about my age. She told us that for several years she'd had hot flashes and an enlarged lymph node on her leg which was dismissed as insignificant. Her previous gynecologist had diagnosed her as menopausal and had even scheduled her for a hysterectomy when another doctor had ordered a blood test and — *voila!* — found lymphoma.

Listening to her story made me wonder what medical schools teach in "Hot Flashes 101," and I thought that it's time to rewrite the syllabus for that course so that every single known cause for hot flashes, including menopause and lymphoma, is taught. Looking beyond gynecological reasons may, in fact, save a life.

I was in for another big surprise that night when Dr. Joseph Himle, Clinical Assistant Professor of Psychology, walked in. Alex had built a home for the Himles before I moved to Michigan, and together we had recently finished building another. I'd gotten to know Joe not as a psychologist, but as a delightful man with a wickedly funny sense of humor, and I wondered if I could sit in the same room with him without laughing.

It turned out that I could, although Joe interjected some humor into his talk where it was appropriate. He described depression as a common side effect of cancer, explained how to recognize it, and offered some advice to combat it. One thing in particular made a strong impression on me. As an example of how powerful our minds can be, he proposed that if each of us were to write on a 3 x 5 card the five things about which we felt most guilty in our lives, and we were to look at that card every hour for a day, we'd probably end up feeling pretty badly. Couldn't we also make ourselves feel better by reminding ourselves of positive things?

At home that night, I found a 3 x 5 card. Reasoning that I could at least manage my mental health even if I couldn't control my physical ailment, I wrote across the top of the card, "If you can worry yourself sick, you can think yourself well," and I listed who and what gave me the greatest joy, starting with Alex, Juli, Skye, Nicholas, and the other family and friends I treasured most. I tucked the card away just in case I might need it, and I made a mental note to call Joe if I even thought that my mental state was collapsing. By the end of the summer, that card would be well worn as I struggled to find beacons of hope.

That night, I also realized that I'd found a place where I could remove my brave person mask and just be me. More than that, I learned that by opening up about my situation, I was opening myself up for help and information. Okay, so it was a little weird listening to perfect strangers talk about constipation, but nobody seemed to think a thing about discussing this common side effect of one of the chemo drugs. Weird or not, meeting others who had gone through treatment didn't alleviate all my fears, but it did help me to think that if others could do it, so, too, could I. And for the first time since the nightmare had begun, I felt that I wasn't alone.

Still, I felt like Rocky getting ready for eight grueling rounds that might knock me to my knees. By the weekend before chemo started, I was ready. At least that's what I wanted everyone to think. The truth is, I hated my body for its attack on me, and I wanted nothing to do with chemotherapy or lymphoma, but I kept telling myself to think about what chemo could do *for* me — like save my life — not what it might do *to* me — like almost kill me first.

Alex, too, was clearly bewildered. He tried to assure me that he was fine, but the sadness in his eyes was unconvincing. I often encouraged him to share his feelings and told him that it was okay to be sad or angry, but he would just put his arms around me and tell me not to worry about him. How could I not? I desperately wanted to alleviate his pain, but he remained stoic and unwilling, or perhaps unable, to verbalize his private agony, for which I felt responsible. I thus felt that I must play his comforter, and yet I could find nothing with which to comfort him.

I believed then, as I do now, that patients' attitudes have a significant effect on how our families and friends react to our illnesses. Consequently, it was my responsibility to create an atmosphere of hope for Alex and others who cared about me, a conviction I tried to sustain, but which sometimes languished under the weight of my own subsequent fears and doubts. But at that time, I yearned for ways to lighten the melodrama so that those around me would find some consolation. Knowing little else to do, I turned to humor, however feeble, to provide temporary relief. Whenever and however I could, I tried to crack jokes to make everyone around me laugh. It was my way of saying, "Everything will be okay." Unfortunately, Alex was never amused by anything I said or did, but there is no doubt that he would have fared worse had I been morose.

I made an appointment to have my hair cut the day after chemo started. That was a big step. When I was seven years old, my mother had cut my hair short and given me a home perm. I'm pretty sure it scarred me for life because I never did have short hair again. Making that appointment was a big deal, but giving up some of my hair, on my own terms, gave me some sense of control over my life and over how much mess I would make when I started to shed.

I even shopped for a wig, though resentful that I had to spend money on something I didn't even want. I hated every one I tried on. They looked and felt awful. The saleswoman failed to tell me they could be trimmed or styled, and I left the store, wigless, in tears.

How long would my hair and I remain connected? Who knew? Everyone is different. Since summer was coming, I decided I'd wear fun, fashionable hats, so I headed to the mall and tried on every one in every store. Have you ever tried to find fashionable hats that actually cover every part of a naked cranium? There are few, and I cursed the milliners for designing perky little fashion statements for only the healthy. Maybe none of them had ever had cancer. I finally found a couple, although I can't say that I was pleased with my purchases.

I worried about how I would maintain our home, which we had recently put on the market with the intention of moving mid-summer. Our move would make the new house our fifth home in seven years. Moving was simply a way of life. Not my way of life, but Alex's.

I'd always teased him that most builders, if not all, must directly descend from nomads who, I theorized, wandered the countryside in search of the most desirable real estate. Despite generations of intermarriage, nomadic genes dominated in descendents who invariably became builders whose real purpose remains the same as their forefathers which is, of course, to acquire the best real estate before someone else does. But without a universally accepted definition of "best," builders continue their quixotic search by frequently changing addresses — which is what we expected to do all too soon again, and I wasn't quite certain how I was supposed to manage it.

The evening before chemo began, Karen called to wish me luck. She also suggested that I prepare a garbage can with a plastic bag so that I could neatly dispose of its contents in case I couldn't make it to the bathroom. Thank you, dear sister, for reminding me of retching.

Karen continued with more practical advice. In case I became sick on the way home, it would be a good idea to take a plastic bag in the car. Sick in the car on the way home? Oh, dear, I hadn't thought about that. If all went as planned, we'd be leaving the hospital at rush hour, and I could just see myself spewing vomit not only in front of Alex, but also for all the passengers in surrounding cars to see. What self-respecting girl does that? Even if chemo finished during daylight hours, surely we shouldn't leave the hospital until after dark.

Juli also called that evening. When I confided my fears to her, she did her best to assure me that Karen was remembering the old days and that newer anti-nausea drugs work pretty well. Great, give me truckloads of those drugs. Juli also promised to send anti-nausea vibes all during the next day. I was so grateful for the pep talk my daughter gave me that night.

Still, Rocky wasn't ready for the fight. Rocky had never wanted this fight in the first place. I went to bed trying to think positive thoughts and trying to practice guided imagery, but fear superseded every good thought. Naturally, I didn't want anyone to know that I had switched into full blown panic mode.

Like me, Alex continued to conceal his real feelings, but he would much later reveal that he had been gearing up, too. Practically, he was working even harder to keep a sharp eye on all the balls he was juggling while trying to make certain that he never stumbled. Emotionally, fear of the unknown was emerging. While I seemed to worry mostly about the initial treatment, he tried to peer beyond it and to formulate a clear plan to help me through the coming months. But as he said later, "How can anyone plan without knowing what to plan for, much less what help you would need?"

At the time, Alex did not want to raise the subject of potential complications that I might not have considered, but he was fully aware that side effects vary widely and hoped that mine would be minimal. He worried that if they took a great physical toll, I might lose my will and that he would not know how to motivate me to keep going. Despite huge efforts to deny all but positive thoughts, those what-ifs he had vowed to suppress were beginning to penetrate his resolve.

● ● ●

Perseverance is not a long race; it is many short races one after another.
— *Walter Elliott*

9. | DOPE-ON-A-ROPE

On April 8, I awoke bargaining with God, as I had so often done in previous weeks. If You want me to undergo chemotherapy, would You please help the chemicals do their job? And one more thing. If it's not too much to ask, could You please keep the side effects to a bare minimum? I really did want to live. And be healthy enough to enjoy life.

I climbed out of bed, went downstairs for coffee and oatmeal, and returned upstairs to prepare myself for my own voluntary metamorphosis into a toxic waste dump. Standing in our closet, I wondered what was appropriate attire for such an occasion. Perhaps something complementary to my own vomit in case it later accessorized my outfit? Comfort reigned supreme, and I chose a comfortable old black pantsuit. Black seemed appropriate. I was, after all, mourning my own good health.

I'd never spent much time counting wrinkles or otherwise self-examining, but that morning, I thoroughly scrutinized the imperfections and faults and furrows on my face. None of them troubled me, but I did wonder if the drugs or the disease would accelerate aging and how long before a shriveled stranger would peer back from the mirror. I was glad we had taken pictures of Alex and me the day before, permanent reminders of life before the ravages of chemo.

Enroute to the hospital by 8:00 a.m., Alex and I chattered about work, but we both knew that it was a feeble attempt to avoid thinking about the inevitable, just moments away. As I looked around at people in the surrounding cars, I thought how lucky they were to be heading to work, to school, to the gym, while I was heading to chemo. And the closer we got to the hospital, the farther away I felt from the healthy world. I would have done anything to turn around, start the day over, and reclaim my place in it.

Digressing from our idle conversation, I asked Alex how he was feeling. "This all seems so surreal," he said. "An out-of-body experience." Funny, that's exactly what I was thinking. Like an episode from *The Twilight Zone*, we were looking down at our other selves going to a place we would never voluntarily go.

For the next several minutes, we were silent. Then, at the traffic light where we would turn into the hospital complex, Alex turned to face me and added that he felt so out of control, so helpless. I'd known that. Men are "fixers." When something breaks, they go to the hardware store, buy the necessary part, bring it home and fix it. And when they can't do that, they feel out of control. I joked that we should run by Stadium Hardware and see if they had some Super-Duper Immune Fixative. Without laughing, he said, "I wish."

In the parking lot, Alex shut off the ignition, turned to me again and sighed. I shifted to face him, smiled, and sighed back. "Okay. How about this? We'll just drop my body off at Dr. Kaminski's Body Repair, you and I will hop a plane for the Caribbean, and we'll pick it up when he's done. What do you think?"

Ignoring my absurdity, he said, "I hate that you have to do this."

"It's not my idea of fun either, but let's go and get it over with." We hugged and walked hand in hand to the clinic.

In the waiting room, Alex leaned over and placed his elbows on his knees and his forehead in the palms of his hands. I rubbed his back and asked what he was thinking. Slowly, he lowered one hand. Still cradling his head in the other, he turned to look up at me. Did

I see a little tear in one eye? He sheepishly grinned and answered, "I think I need a drink."

"Have one for me," I replied.

We met with Dr. Kaminski and Judy one final time before chemo. They asked if we had any more questions, but we were too numb to think of any. Both wished us well and assured us they would be nearby if we needed them.

When we checked in at the infusion desk, the receptionist gave me a message from Juli. It said, "Remember the vibes I'm sending you today. Good luck. I love you." My eyes dampened, and I clutched that note for a very long time that day.

The Lymphoma Clinic and the infusion area share a reception area, so I had been there before. But suddenly, I wondered if everyone would be tossing their cookies. Would the whole place reek? I almost gagged just thinking about it.

I tried to keep my spirits up and to think positively. Silently, I repeated jokes I had cracked. I had even brought work to review with Alex — anything to take my mind off the pollutants that would soon enter my body. I was anxious to slay the cancer as soon as possible, but on the other hand, I was apprehensive about chemo's side effects. Apprehension was winning.

I had to go to the bathroom. Once I left Alex, my eyes filled with tears and I stared straight down so that no one would see. Without looking, I pushed open the bathroom door and walked to the first stall. There I sat, tears and pee flowing in perfect sync. I hadn't heard the door open, but I suddenly realized that there was a strong flow going outside the stall. It didn't sound quite right. Then I heard the door open again. Footsteps. A man's voice. Another man's voice and another strong flow.

How was I going to get out of this predicament? Maybe I could just wait until they left and no one would be any wiser. I lifted my feet off the floor so they wouldn't see shoes that no man would wear. Couldn't they just finish and leave? Should I flush and flee? One man left, and I thought the other would be out of there soon and that I could escape unnoticed. But then another man came in. I'll never get out of here, I thought, not without being seen. Finally, I put my head down, opened the stall door and ran, mumbling "Sorry" as I bolted through the door. I dashed to the couch where Alex was sitting and buried my head in his shoulder, whimpering "I just went into the men's room."

"What did you do that for?" he asked. As I explained how it happened, he shook his head, put his arm around me and tried to comfort me. Was I already losing my ability to function in a normal world? Would I need to have Alex walk me to a bathroom? And why couldn't they call my name now? How long would I have to sit in that waiting room with the men who had seen me dash out of the men's room?

I froze when my name finally was called. I looked at Alex and thought if I just didn't answer, we could silently escape down the elevator and forget about all this.

Looking back, I wish I had asked Dr. Kaminski or Judy for a tour of the infusion area before chemo began. I would have seen that it was not the torture chamber I had envisioned. Instead, the bright semi-circular room was lined with reclining chairs. Patients, some awake and some asleep, were attached to IV's. No one was sick and the room had no odor. An aide escorted us to my own recliner where I settled in with a mixture of trepidation and hope.

A nurse stopped by, made small talk about her children and her job, asked about mine, and otherwise did her best to assure me that I would be just fine. Another aide came and offered to bring us a bagel or juice. I hadn't expected room service — rather, chairside service.

Alex sat facing me, clearly wondering what to expect. Silently, he was thinking that he wished this was all behind us. He wanted to remain optimistic and thought to himself, "This better work." But he had read enough to understand that no chemo comes with a guarantee. Since I had never expressed that concern, he certainly didn't want to raise that unhappy possibility, and he tried to banish the thought from his mind in order to hide his worry from me. But there was no hiding his worry. The anguish in his eyes clearly told me how difficult it was for him to watch a stranger pump my body full of lethal chemicals.

There was no escape now, for him or for me, so I surrendered to the inescapable. I winced as the nurse inserted the IV and hung the bag of chemicals. With a smile, I gave Alex the thumbs up sign, pointed to the drugs hanging high above my shoulder, fondled the tube through which they dripped, and declared with conviction, "This Dope-On-A-Rope gives me lots of hope." Indeed, that bag was the SWAT team sent to massacre a vulnerable enemy. At least I hoped it was vulnerable.

Within minutes, my eyelids became heavy, and my mind drifted to images of myself as a gray-haired old lady walking hand in hand with Alex on a beach. Warm, foamy waves gently lapped at our feet while seagulls cried overhead. That's the last I remember before falling asleep.

I neither threw up nor saw anyone who did. I was groggy when we left the hospital, but relieved that nothing horrible had happened. I didn't even feel queasy. And when I awoke the next morning, I was surprised that I felt no different than I had the previous morning. How anti-climactic can you get?

Alex called as I was leaving for my hair appointment. "I've decided to shave my head in solidarity," he proudly proclaimed.

"Thanks," I laughed, "but don't even think about it."

"I'll do it," he repeated.

"No way," I insisted. He didn't, thank goodness. I would have felt badly had he taken that extra step because I knew how sensitive he was about his thinning hair. And he was supporting me in a myriad of other, more useful ways.

As my hairdresser began to shear, I nervously awaited the outcome. Within minutes, several inches of locks lay on the floor, and for the second day in a row, I stared at the image in the mirror, startled by the person with such short hair staring back. Was that really me?

I disliked the cut less than I'd expected. And most importantly, I had smugly established exactly who was in charge by removing most of my hair before chemo had the chance.

When Alex first saw me with my new look, he smiled and said, "Hey, you look like Jamie Lee Curtis. Pretty chic." As I encountered friends and acquaintances, they all told me how much younger I looked. I wondered how old I'd looked before and thought that maybe I should have cut my hair years ago. It certainly reduced the time it took to get ready in the mornings.

I grew accustomed to the Chemo Cut in no time, but I did expect my eyelashes to depart and along with them, those pesky little chins hairs that I was forever plucking. That isn't what happened, though. My eyelashes thinned but stayed and those little chin hairs mistook chemo for Miracle Gro and multiplied profusely. Go figure.

About five days after the first treatment, chemo made its presence known. Let's just say that I drank an ocean of prune juice for two days before resorting to Milk of Magnesia and joking about teaching United Van Lines a thing or two about moving.

Friends delivered mouthwatering dinners over the next few days and weeks. I was a little embarrassed and self-conscious, but also deeply humbled by the attention, especially from people I considered acquaintances. I didn't know it yet, but cancer would teach me to accept help in many forms from many people. It would also teach me that family, friends, acquaintances and even strangers welcomed the opportunity to participate in my healing.

My mother always taught me that when we keep busy and think of others, we have less time to dwell on our own problems. I decided to put her theory to the test as never before. I wrote notes to old friends. I sent funny cards for no reason at all. I baked cookies and cakes for the nurses who drew blood and administered the chemo and for the doctors and their staffs who cared for me. I continued doing these things throughout my treatment, and it did help to lift my spirits. It wasn't until months later that I realized that my efforts were also my way of reminding people that I was still me, not just a blob of cancer.

During the first cycle of chemo, Alex and I were greatly relieved that our fears about side effects didn't materialize. I didn't once feel queasy. My hair remained affixed to my head, but I did buy a wig, although I hated it. I continued to work and to lead a perfectly normal life, interrupted only by regular blood draws. Judy kept me well informed that my counts were falling and rising as expected. When the time for the second treatment arrived, three weeks after the first, I was a seasoned chemo pro, and I waltzed into the infusion area perfectly happy to have life-saving toxins enter my body.

Two weeks later, those life-saving toxins began to take their toll. One morning, I went upstairs to dress, found our cat curled at the foot of our bed, curled up around him — just to give him a quick hug before showering — and fell sound asleep. It wasn't even nine in the morning. No wonder Alex was startled when he stopped by the house to retrieve a forgotten file.

The following morning, I spread blueprints out on the dining room table to mark some changes on them. I don't remember drifting off, but Alex found me sound asleep in the chair with my head on the table.

I looked forward to having dinner with friends and swore to myself that I would stay awake to enjoy their company, but sometime during the meal, I dozed off, still sitting in their dining room chair. They and Alex continued to eat and converse — without me — and it took all of them to awaken me at the end of the evening. I joked that at least I hadn't fallen into my plate, but inside, I fumed that I could no longer count on my body to perform the simple task of staying awake. It seemed to be carrying me farther and farther away from my normal life, no matter how hard I tried to stop it.

A week before the third cycle, fever complemented exhaustion. Judy asked me to come to the clinic right away and suggested I plan for a hospital stay. I'd developed neutropenia, a side effect of chemotherapy resulting from lowered neutrophils, our primary defense against infection. In plain English, my immune system was unable to fend off normal worldly germs.

I was sent directly to a private cell in the hospital where I would have contact with no one except nurses and doctors. Large doses of antibiotics were pumped into me, and since other patients were out of sight, they were also out of mind. I still did not consider myself particularly ill, although I was. I was simply in some clinical hideaway for a small adjustment. It was an inconvenient but short incarceration of two days. Nothing more, nothing less.

One incident during my stay, however, astounded me. Alex, sitting in the chair beside my bed, asked a nurse whether cancer could be contracted through bodily fluids. I sat straight up and stared at him in disbelief. There sat an intelligent man who had read about cancer and who should have known that he couldn't catch it from a kiss. Months later I would learn that his fear was common, though unfounded. Cancer is not contagious. I guess Alex simply needed reassurance.

His other fears also surfaced. Although he hoped this would be our only complication, he had already realized that the road to recovery was going to be much harder than he had anticipated, and he searched himself for additional resolve with which to steel himself against further difficulties. Of course he did not share those thoughts with me at the time. He was too busy trying to wear his mask of optimism.

Although exhausted, I was delighted to return home from the hospital, but two days later, another fever arose and pain pierced my midsection. By midday, when I literally crawled up the stairs on all fours, I reluctantly called Judy, afraid that she would tell me to return to the clinic prepared for another hospital stay, which is exactly what she did.

Within minutes, Alex dropped what he was doing and was home to take me to the hospital for the second time that week. Just before leaving, I withdrew our home from the Multiple Listing Service and removed the For Sale sign from the yard. Somehow I knew it would be impossible to continue showing the house, at least for awhile. Packing, moving and unpacking was inconceivable. Alex's nomadic wanderlust would have to wait. The chasm between me and the healthy world was about to break wide open.

● ● ●

When you're going through hell, keep going.
— *Winston Churchill*

10. | HOTEL HELL

A t the hospital, my pain and I were deposited into a wheelchair. I was horrified that I was incapable of walking beside Alex as he pushed me to the eighth floor where double doors signified, in no uncertain terms, how sick Dr. Kaminski thought I was. A sign on them said, "Hematology Oncology Unit/Bone Marrow Transplant/Restricted Area." Restricted from what? I'd never been on a floor in a hospital where doors separated patients from the general hospital population, and I choked up, wondering what was in store for me behind them. Alex knelt down and put his arms around me, trying to comfort me, but I felt like a repeat offender entering San Quentin. Worse, for the first time I saw myself for what I really was — sick. Really sick.

Alex and I were escorted to a semi-private cell where I would be excluded from life for ten days. In no time, I figured out that semi-private is an oxymoron. There is nothing private about a hospital, and they take the expression "No rest for the weary" to literal extremes. Day and night, carts clang, bells ring and the PA system blares. Doze off and you'll be nudged awake for a test, a medication, a poke or a prod. But at least there's room service. Three square meals a day include at least one of the five main food groups: fast, frozen, foul, flat or unfit for human consumption. All this for $2,500 a day. No wonder I called the place Hotel Hell.

I scarcely settled into my room before a nurse thrust in an IV, to which I would be securely affixed for the duration of my visit. Complications everyone hopes to avoid went from bad to worse. If I had escaped feeling ill before, my reprieve was up. I felt horrible. The pain in my midsection was diagnosed as an infarct, or the death of part of my spleen. Just great, I thought. My body had decided I deserved a slow death and would kill me one part at a time. Then pneumonia set in. Worse, my cancer cells were overachievers: chemotherapy wasn't slowing them at all. When a stronger combination of drugs was administered, renal failure followed, the result of tumor lysis syndrome which can arise when the contents of tumor cells are released as the cells are destroyed. None of this was my idea of fun.

My first roommate, who arrived shortly after I did, was an older lady whose husband never left her bedside day or night. They kept the curtain between us drawn at all times and hardly spoke to each other, much less to me.

Alex, Lisa, Ted, Zan and Greta visited throughout the weekend. Lisa hugged me and joked, "You better get well. I'm counting on you to take care of me." Without having any idea how I would deliver, I promised her that I would. Alex's face, blank and drawn, revealed his anxiety. He seemed remote, almost aloof. When I suggested he sit on the foot of the bed for lack of available chairs, he chose instead to stand. Although he said he was more comfortable standing — and knowing Alex, he probably was — I interpreted his physical distance of a few feet as miles of emotional distance. Only when everyone was leaving did he approach, and then only long enough to give me a cursory kiss on the forehead.

Alex would later tell me that he had thought he had understood the seriousness of my illness before I landed in the hospital the second time, but he began to grasp its real danger as he watched me begin to spiral downward physically. Where I would stop was anyone's guess, and his own confidence and optimism plummeted with each new physical complication. Unable to sleep, he turned to Jack Daniels for assistance, but found little.

Alex genuinely wanted to hide his fears from me, but even his stoicism made it difficult to manage a smile when he had no idea how far I would fall. Or how far he would. He resolved to be as encouraging to me as his remaining strength would allow, but he also feared that he would crumble if he came too close to me — and that was something he did not want me to see.

By the third night in Hotel Hell, I felt more wretched than ever. I rarely dream, or at least I don't remember dreams, but in the middle of that night, I had the most vivid dream I can ever remember. In full technicolor, I saw my father with his arms folded just as he had often held them. We were separated only by a narrow stream. He assured me, "Don't worry, everything is very comfortable where I am." I was sure Daddy was telling me that I would soon cross that stream and join him.

I awakened from that specter of death unnerved and terrified. Until then, death had been abstract but it suddenly seemed so imminent, and I'd never felt so totally alone. I needed Alex, but I couldn't reach the phone. Instead I called the nurse. Waiting for her, I wrote "Call Alex" on a notepad that I could reach, but no one called Alex in the middle of the night, and to this day, I am not certain how much distress I was in.

I remember very little about the following day except that the dream haunted me. As much as I loved my father, I was hardly ready for a reunion. Several months later, Alex told me that I begged him not to keep me alive on life support. I reminded him that the hospital had a copy of my living will. Make sure they remember it, I demanded of him. I have no memory of that conversation, but Alex grew terrified that my will was slipping away.

I do remember that oxygen was added to my daily regimen. The tubes in my nose were reminders that I could no longer accomplish the small feat of breathing alone. I felt like I was losing control of my own destiny.

Alex must have called my old friend Noreen that day because she flew up from Florida the next. When she and Alex entered the room, I was surprised to see her, but she walked over to my bed and demanded, as only a good friend can, "I didn't fly all this way to wait on you hand and foot. Now get your ass up out of that bed." All I could muster was, "Screw you." She laughed. I managed a chuckle.

Noreen became Alex's assistant cheerleader who stayed with me when he couldn't. Still, he was torn between wanting to ignore everything except me and knowing that he had to keep the business afloat. Guilt gnawed at him when he wasn't by my side.

Alex and Noreen both did countless things that said, "You aren't alone. You've got a big load, but we're here to help you carry it." They screened phone calls, brought in whatever I wanted from home, fetched drinks. They let me whine a little, or a lot, and then made me walk — okay, shuffle — one more lap around the hall when I would rather have quit.

My second roommate arrived the same day Noreen did. She was a spunky 29-year-old woman with lupus and bladder cancer and tubes and pain. She and I tried to keep our spirits up while our friends and family visited, but at night, in the darkness, we shared the common experience of cancer that only cancer patients can know. We talked about its indignities the way others might talk about the inconvenience of having a dead battery. She regretted that she would probably never marry and have children. When she casually and matter-of-factly brought up the subject of dying, I joined in the conversation without difficulty. For the first time in my life, I actually spoke, to an almost total stranger, about death — my own. It was deeply depressing.

Five days after entering Hotel Hell, Dr. Kaminski reached into his arsenal and brought out a more full-bodied chemotherapy called CHOP, which is CVP with the addition of adriamycin, a drug which can damage the heart, so this combination of drugs can be administered a maximum of eight times, and then only once in a lifetime. Translated, I was about to burn an option bridge.

Wondering if CHOP would be any more successful than CVP, I asked Dr. Kaminski to evaluate my odds. I should have known he's too smart to fall into that trap. With optimistic compassion, he simply answered, "We still have many options." I wanted him to be more specific, knowing fully that he couldn't. How could I expect Dr. Kaminski to know how long I'd be around?

Alex stayed with me long after the first CHOP treatment was over. I was so groggy that I remember little about his presence. Months later, he recalled sitting in the darkness of my room, his resolve to stay positive and strong shattered by the avalanche of complications I was suffering. He feared the worst, tried to the believe the best, and finally decided it would be best not to feel. Anything. He told himself that he needed simply to exist in order to face potential subsequent setbacks. While he wanted to believe that each tomorrow would bring improvement, he could find no solid evidence on which to build that hope. CVP had failed. There was no guarantee that CHOP would succeed. What if it didn't?

Almost immediately, CHOP began to work nearly too well. Lickety-split, the cells that had been trying to kill me began to die, but they were dumping their contents into me faster than my kidneys could get rid of the waste. Renal failure followed. It was about as much fun as it sounds.

In order to counteract that complication, Dr. Kaminski decided to blow me up like a balloon. Industrial strength Sani-Flush, otherwise known as saline, was aggressively pumped into me to flush out my kidneys, but my body couldn't eliminate the solution as quickly as it flowed into me. Within hours, my poor body was bloated with about twenty extra pounds — pounds that stretched the skin on my thighs and abdomen so tight I thought it would rip. The weight was evenly distributed from my head to my feet — almost. It completely missed my chest, and Noreen and I laughed that not a single ounce found its way there. We considered scolding Dr. Kaminski for this oversight, but decided not to embarrass him.

At least that's what I'd thought until six months later when Noreen told me what really happened. "There you were half dead and all you worried about was pumping up your boobs." Breaking into laughter, she added, "You gave Dr. Kaminski hell about it, too."

"No way," I insisted.

"Oh yeah, you kept telling him you wanted a vote in where you got pumped up."

"I didn't say that to him," I declared, twisting my face in disbelief.

"Oh, you did," she convinced me. I groaned, put my head in my hand, laughed with mild embarrassment, and persuaded myself that he has heard worse from other drug-drenched patients.

I may have been joking around that day, but Alex was at his wit's end. My failing kidneys annihilated whatever remaining control he had managed to maintain over his emotions. By the time he left the hospital that evening, he was distraught. At home, he and Noreen discussed the situation over a couple of drinks. Alex had far more than a couple, and I would eventually learn from both of them that alcohol and emotions and exhaustion fueled an argument that night.

Alex told Noreen he was glad she was there, but he couldn't understand why this was happening to him or to me. It was so unfair. He felt helpless by an illness over which he had no control. And with complications striking one blow after another, how could he possibly manage the company, Zan, Greta and life in general while finding the time and mental strength to support me? Finally, he lashed out at Noreen that she would be with me for a week, but that he would be stuck with the long-term consequences, whatever they may be. Wrestling with her own fears and thinking that Alex wouldn't be stuck with anything if I didn't pull out soon, she lashed back, "Alex, this isn't about you. It's about Betsy."

Uncharacteristically angry, Alex stormed out of the house. Noreen panicked, knowing that he shouldn't be driving, but unsure of where he might go and unfamiliar with Ann Arbor, she could do nothing but hope he would return safely and soon. She went upstairs to bed but lay awake in the darkness until she heard the back door slam shut. I shuddered when both Alex and Noreen later told me of this incident, and I thanked whatever angel had ridden with Alex that night.

Over coffee the next morning, both regretted their argument, and they agreed to work together to help me heal, one specific step at a time. Dr. Kaminski wanted me up and walking, and Noreen would see to it that I was. He also wanted to make sure that I ate properly, so both would make sure that I had food that appealed to me. Little did they know that their resolution to champion my diet would be a monumental challenge. The medications had fried my taste buds, and no matter what room service delivered, breakfast, lunch and dinner smelled and tasted repulsive.

Alex and Noreen brought in one thing after another, to no avail. Nearly everything tasted like salt or metal, and I could scarcely bear to eat. Even Oreos tasted vile. And what is life without Oreos?

As for my appearance, I didn't even recognize myself. No amount of makeup, even if I had tried to wear it, could have camouflaged my bloated faced or widened the slits my eyes had become. I looked so bad that a friend's uncle, who was also a patient on the floor, mistook Noreen for my daughter. People used to mistake us for sisters. I'd never considered myself particularly vain, but I wanted no one to see me this way — not Alex, not Noreen, not a nurse, not a doctor. But what was a girl to do?

In my previous life, my daily routine had been anything but routine. Unfettered to any particular office, I met clients or potential clients at various sites. I searched suppliers for whatever our clients dreamed up. I planned the next marketing blitz and attended various meetings. If illness had distanced me from this ordinary life, my stay in Hotel Hell severed me from it completely. Confined to half a room, dependent on drugs and oxygen, I was robbed of my health, my freedom and, I feared, of my future.

Meanwhile, the world outside was going on, and apparently going on just fine. As chair of the Sales and Marketing Council of the local homebuilders association, I should have been at the biggest event of the year, but someone quickly filled my shoes and it took place without me. And when Alex sold one of our homes late in the week, I should have been happy, but I felt cheated out of doing my job. I sold our homes. He built them. That's the way things were supposed to be. But my illness had broken my connection to everything normal, and I hated my body for its utter failure. Worse, I was glimpsing my world without me — and it never seemed to skip a beat.

The IV's were regularly changed in order to avoid infection at any given site, and my blood was drawn twice daily. My bruised arms were evidence of patienthood, and there were so many holes in me that I was sure I would spring a leak. And just what did the hospital do with all the blood it amassed? Noreen and I imagined that secret pagan rituals were being held somewhere.

Early each morning, Grand Marshal Dr. Kaminski led a parade of four or five residents into my room. Together, they examined me, assessed the previous day and night's developments, and planned whatever they deemed appropriate for the upcoming day and night. During the parade, the residents always walked quietly in perfect step behind the grand marshal. But when he was back in the clinic or the classroom or wherever his schedule took him, one or another of the residents returned later during the day and evening. And then they weren't so quiet. In fact, they let their personalities shine brightly. One glowed when he spoke of his soon-to-be-bride, and I couldn't help but smile with him. Early one morning, another slipped quietly into my room, saw tears falling from my closed eyes, sat in the chair beside my bed and lifted my hand gently before I even knew she was there.

It occurred to me that medicine is one of the few occupations that still values apprenticeship, and residents really are apprentices. They've nearly completed grueling training in the latest and greatest medical techniques and therapies, but still report to a grand marshal, otherwise known as an attending physician. Teaching hospitals are much too modest about this service, and I thought about offering to write an ad campaign for them. The headline would read, "Huge Sale on Medical Services. Buy Four — Sometimes Five or Six — Geniuses for The Price of One!" In a teaching hospital, that's exactly what you get. It's the best deal around.

And the nurses? They not only faithfully carried out the doctors' orders but also took the time to make small talk, a gesture that recognized me as a human being with a life outside the hospital. Every one of them gave me an extra dose of kindness along with the medications they administered.

Judy, too, stopped by periodically and always brought her caring gentleness that I had come to know so well. And she always sensed my frame of mind immediately and knew exactly what to say to leave me feeling better than she found me.

By week's end, I desperately wanted Alex to hold me close, and when he still didn't, I assumed that he was repulsed by my appearance and felt awkward coming near me and my tubes. Even in my drugged stupor, I could clearly see that he was physically exhausted and emotionally drained, and I felt terrible for causing him so much stress. Lightly, I reminded him to get a full medical report on anyone he dated after I was gone. He simply shook his head and stared blankly back at me.

Many months later, I asked Alex how much my physical appearance had repulsed him. "It didn't in the slightest," he replied.

"Right," I sarcastically shot back.

"Repulse is the wrong word," he reflected. "Your physical appearance told me how sick you were. I was never repulsed by it. I was scared to death, and if I'd crawled onto your bed and held you in my arms, I'd have lost it — and that was the last thing you needed."

That was a big admission from someone who rarely expresses his feelings, and I replied, "If I'm ever in that condition again, will you skip the macho stuff and just hold me?" He promised he would.

By the end of the first week, I began to lobby aggressively to go home. Like a spoiled child, I repeatedly begged Dr. Kaminski to release me, and like a patient parent, he repeatedly explained that my blood counts and kidney function had to normalize first. If I had been in his shoes, I might have screamed at me, "What part of 'no' don't you understand?"

As I entered the second weekend in Hotel Hell, I was desperate for fresh air. I begged Alex to smuggle me out just for an hour, to take me for a ride anywhere. He wouldn't have, of course, but his excuse was that we couldn't fit the IV pole in the car. I moaned that I would hold it out the window. When Dr. Kaminski visited, I jokingly threatened to break a window if I couldn't breathe some air soon. The good doctor gave me a pass to walk to the courtyard. Walk? Given the size of the hospital complex, the courtyard was much too far to walk in my condition. Noreen rounded up a wheelchair and, with IV pole in tow, pushed me to freedom, or at least as much freedom as I had known in a week. Outside, I took a deep breath, and the fragrance of spring flowers and fresh grass was intoxicating.

Noreen spread a sheet on the grass and we sprawled out to sunbathe as we'd often done in years past. Only in years past, we'd sunbathed in bathing suits, at the ocean's edge or poolside — a world and a lifetime away from sunbathing in pajamas and robe, attached to an IV pole by a tube in my arm that was barely long enough to allow me to lie down. Weird tan lines, huh?

We may not have been the bathing beauties we had once fancied ourselves, but the sun warmed my body and spirit. As I looked around at other patients in wheelchairs and bathrobes, attached to their own IV poles, I couldn't help but ask rhetorically, "This scene is straight out of *One Flew Over the Cuckoo's Nest.* What the hell are we doing here?" How far we were from our younger, carefree days.

Close to midnight that night, I was hungry for the first time in days, a good sign I presumed. Alex had left food for me in the refrigerator in the patient lounge at the end of the hall, so my pole and I lumbered down to retrieve some morsels. On the way, I passed a door on which a large handwritten note said, "No crying allowed." The patient inside was dying, and I had no way of knowing that his daughter and son-in-law were sleeping in the lounge. Only they weren't sleeping. When I flipped on the light, I found them on the couch making love. Oops. As quickly as I could, I flipped off the light, shut the door, and plodded back to my room. Hungry and envious, I crawled into my own bed tearfully aching for Alex. Lymphoma had long since clobbered our own intimacy.

In the darkness, a thousand what-ifs rushed at me at once. I was no longer the person Alex had fallen in love with, much less married. Would he have fallen in love with me knowing I had lymphoma? Of course not, I decided. And what if I didn't recover? I didn't want Alex to spend the rest of his life alone, but neither did I want him to spend it with some other woman — it was me I wanted him to spend it with. But what was left of me? Nothing. I had become everything I had never wanted to be. The tears I shed that night could have created a whole new body of water. It might have been named "The Sea of Self-Pity."

At last, on Memorial Day morning, Dr. Kaminski released me from Hotel Hell. That name was a reflection of my own frustrations, not of the people who worked there. If I had named it for them, it would have been Paradise Palace or something equally complimentary. Without a doubt, every person — from the doctors to the residents to the nurses to the aides — did his or her best to treat me in the most humane and respectful way. None of them ever treated me as an object or as a task to be completed. Instead, all seemed acutely aware that their tenderness made a palpable difference in my comfort, if not my recovery. Their extraordinary kindness helped me to maintain some measure of sanity.

When I reflect back on my hospital stay, I realize that I was at least drugged much of the time. Alex had faced reality cold. He did the best he could, but sitting in a hospital day after day, watching someone you love suffer, takes an enormous toll, and every one of my physical failures had tightened the emotional noose around his neck. It would take some time for him to breathe comfortably again.

Despite Alex, Noreen and the remarkable hospital staff, I had simply become a caged animal. I'd endured ten days of boredom, punctuated by fear and self-pity. I'd wondered if I would ever reclaim my ordinary life. Did I dare to expect CHOP to succeed? And a future? I wasn't even certain I'd be around to wear the summer sandals I had bought on sale the previous winter. My body was intact, but the rest of me felt mortally wounded.

● ● ●

Life is not a matter of holding good cards,
but of playing a poor hand well.
— Robert Louis Stevenson

11. | GOODBYE HAIR, HELLO MANGE

Returning home was like going to the Ritz. Never mind that housekeeping had overlooked the place for a couple of weeks. It's not that Alex hadn't tried to straighten up, but how many hours are there in the day after working, preparing my take-out meals, and visiting the sick ward? To me, home looked like a palace, our kitty and I were overjoyed at our reunion, and I could get back to life. To celebrate my homecoming, we had a cookout with Lisa, Ted and friends. Still bloated, I'm sure I looked resplendent in my stretchiest stretch pants.

I hadn't had a decent night's sleep in ten days, and I was deliriously overjoyed to crawl high up into our antique double bed that night. I had hoped that Alex would hold me close in the darkness. Instead, he immediately fell asleep on his own side of the bed. Continents, rather than inches, seemed to separate us.

Alex was truly worn out. Months later he would tell me that he had been the leader of my emotional battle as well as everyone else's — self-appointed, of course. When his parents and children, my sister and daughter and friends had worried about me during my hospitalization, he had considered it his job to keep everyone focused on a positive outcome. He had repeatedly tried to convince them that my complications were only a temporary setback, and he had tried to assure them that losing a battle didn't mean we were losing the war, even though the war wasn't going according to plan.

Alex hadn't, however, fully believed his own words, and he'd withdrawn further into himself searching for hope and strength and a remedy for his own wounds. Of course he was relieved that I'd checked out of Hotel Hell, but the setbacks had traumatized him so deeply that his raw emotions required time to heal, just as my body did. At least he broke off his relationship with Jack Daniels.

Noreen returned to Florida the day after my release, and I returned to the couch — again. I slept and slept, and when I was awake, all I wanted to do was sleep.

At the end of the week, Alex and I — born three years and a day apart — would celebrate our birthdays, and we definitely view birthdays differently. I think they are important rituals to celebrate each year of life while they remind Alex of aging. I'd always had trouble understating his birthday to his satisfaction, and he'd never managed to do enough on mine. Both of us usually got it wrong and managed to offend each other.

Three days after my release, on Alex's birthday, I was back in the clinic, exhausted and frustrated that my body was not cooperating and letting me get back to living normally. Judy voiced concern that I might be becoming depressed. Who? Me? Of course not. Despite my vow to recognize and seek help for depression should it occur, I couldn't see the forest for the trees.

Physically, I was anemic. Chemo had wiped out not only the cancer cells but also the healthy ones that our bodies need to function properly. A blood transfusion would hopefully replace them and jumpstart my body from its inertia. Hours later, well past dinner, we arrived home. A single candle pushed into a cookie was a poor substitute for the cake I had wanted to bake for Alex that day, but at least Zan and I sang "Happy Birthday" and gave him our presents and cards. For the first time, Alex's birthday was low-key, but another day at the hospital gave him no reason to believe that recovery was imminent. He wondered if it was even possible.

I spent most of the following day — my birthday — dozing on the couch and looking forward to Alex coming home after work. More than any year before, I was thankful to be alive and thrilled to have a birthday. Alex got it all wrong. At least I thought he did.

Unquestionably, I was in no shape to do anything, but I had thought of suggesting that we go out for ice cream after dinner. However, I never got the chance to bring it up. I was on the phone with Juli when Alex motioned that he was going shopping with Zan and a friend who was spending the night. They quickly disappeared before I could collect my thoughts. When I did, I couldn't believe that he had left me behind to rot on the couch. It was my birthday, for Pete's sake!

Alex and the boys arrived home around ten o'clock and told me about their outing which had included stopping for ice cream. And then Alex went to bed, but not before handing me a note which said "I give you my karma. Happy Birthday." I was furious. No, I was seething. I had wanted to celebrate life, and they had left me out completely. And all Alex gave me was a handwritten note giving me that which cannot be given away. Never mind that Alex does have good karma. He's the luckiest man alive. If he were a rooster in a hen house, I am sure he would lay eggs. But did he think I wouldn't be around long enough to make giving me a real gift — no matter how small — senseless? Did he think I was going to die? I seemed to have forgotten that the best gifts never come wrapped.

Well, I wasn't going to die, and I was going to enjoy at least some familiar birthday ritual, even if I had to do it all by myself. But how? For the first time in two weeks, I got in my car and drove — stewing — around the neighborhood for a few minutes. When I got home, I placed a candle into another cookie and then, in a pathetic act of self-pity, took it into our bedroom. Alex was already sleeping, so I woke him up while I sang "Happy Birthday to Me." Sleepily, he said nothing more than "What are you doing?" before rolling over and going back to sleep. Oh, how very sensitive. I might have entitled that night in our life, "Crazed Former Inmate Goes Berserk."

I sobbed myself to sleep on the couch that night and was not exactly happy the next morning. Alex couldn't understand why. He insisted that he had asked me if I wanted to go out for ice cream and that I had declined. Since I had seemed so tired, he had thought it would be good to get boisterous boys out of the house so that I could rest. Anyway, his mother was planning a birthday dinner for us both on Sunday. What was a couple of days?

In retrospect, and knowing Alex, he probably did mention ice cream, and given my dopey state of mind, I probably didn't remember — which of course makes me look like the self-absorbed prima donna that I was. I did, in fact, pout for a couple of days before finally realizing that Alex has never done a malicious thing in his life. And we did have a birthday party two days later, through which I mostly slept.

A week later Alex's dad Ted would turn 90. Months earlier, we had invited some of his out-of-state friends for a surprise party and they were planning to make the trip. Some of our friends were also coming, but in my condition, how was I supposed to host a party? Alex had called our friends while I was in the hospital and asked each of them to bring a dish. All I would have to do was straighten and decorate the house.

During the next week, I did a little housekeeping — a little — each day. In my previous life, I would have blitzed through the house from top to bottom in no time. I suppose I could have hired help, but that would have meant admitting my own frailty. Forcing myself to get up and perform even mundane chores boosted my spirits and probably my energy. And Alex and Zan pitched in, as they always do.

My body deflated slightly each day so that by week's end, I could squeeze into most of my wardrobe. I resembled my old self — sort of.

The afternoon of June 8 arrived, and guests filled our home for the first time in months. The table was laden with delicious food, and the house was at least presentable. When Ted arrived, he was taken aback by the presence of so many familiar faces, gathered to honor his long and healthy life. It was a lovely party, one which he thoroughly enjoyed. I couldn't imagine my next birthday, much less having 40 more.

Two days later I received my first treatment of Rituxan, a monoclonal antibody which binds to the surface antigen CD20 on the cancerous cells and recruits the body's immune system to destroy them. Adding Rituxan to chemotherapy had proven very promising.

Benadryl, administered prior to Rituxan in order to counteract potential flu-like symptoms, put me to sleep. About half way through the infusion, I developed fever and chills, expected side effects often associated with the first Rituxan treatment. Judy immediately came to check on me, interrupted the infusion, ordered drugs to offset the symptoms, and then restarted the Rituxan when they subsided. Hours later, I went home. Two days later, the second CHOP treatment would hopefully slaughter more cancer cells.

Still trying desperately to regain energy and strength two and a half weeks after my release, I'd earned the title "Champion Couch Potato of the World." I simply couldn't make it through a day without napping, sometimes in the mornings, sometimes in the afternoons, often both. How could I plan a meeting or anything else without having confidence in my ability to perform the simple task of staying awake?

And then there was Alex, always ready, willing and able to take me to whatever appointment or test I had. Always willing to cook dinner, do the laundry, and make the phone calls I should have made. And lately, always remote. It wasn't that he was ever mean-spirited. He simply moved about in a trance, his eyes hollow and his smile but a memory. I was somewhat aware of his own anxiety, but too overwhelmed by my own to be of much help. Sometimes I felt like we were on different planets.

Alex needed a break from this nightmare as much as I did. Fortunately one was approaching. For fourteen years during the third week in June, he had taken the kids to Camp Michigania, a camp in northern Michigan for U of M alumni and their families. I was unable to go, but there was no reason for him or the kids to miss out. The week at camp had always recharged his batteries, and I wondered if it would have the same effect this year. Or was the stress of this year simply too much to overcome in one week?

Alex had called Karen while I was in the hospital and had asked if she would stay with me during the week he would be gone. When he had asked, Mother was also in the hospital, although she did not tell him — or me. At the time, she had feared losing us both but had promised him she would come. With the weight of a different world on her shoulders, she must have certainly wondered how she would manage to be there for me and our mother at the same time.

By the time Karen came to babysit me, Mother felt well enough to come along. They arrived two days before Alex left, and by that time, I was certain I could have stayed alone, but knowing that I was in good hands if I needed them, Alex could leave guilt-free, and I was happy for the company.

Before he left, we hugged, holding each other closer than we had in weeks. Still, it was clear to me that while our bodies were close, we were separated by our own private agonies. This trip, I hoped, would restore his energy and improve his outlook. While he was gone, I vowed that I would try even harder to regain my own energy and reclaim my optimism.

That vow would quickly be tested. About four hours after Alex left, I was standing in the kitchen, slicing peaches into a bowl when I thought I caught a glimpse of something falling past my right eye. Something was falling, all right — *my hair!* A few strands hit the counter, but most landed in the bowl atop the peaches. Without thinking, I laid down the knife and grabbed my head, whereupon my scalp surrendered more hair to my sticky, juice-covered hand. Kinda gives new meaning to peach fuzz, doesn't it?

I wanted to scream. But Mother and Karen were nearby, and I really didn't want to share that moment with anyone. So I screamed silently — very loudly. Fortunately, they were watching a movie with their backs turned to me. Quietly, I pitched the hairy concoction, wrapped a kitchen towel around my head so that I wouldn't leave a trail, and escaped upstairs unnoticed.

In the bathroom, I stared at the bald spot, grimaced, and made several primeval groans before trying to convince myself that temporary baldness was a small price to pay for my life. I then slipped a knit cap over my head to catch the mess, returned downstairs and went straight to the dictionary.

With its help earlier in the year, I had fumbled my way through Medicalese, a prerequisite for understanding any medical malfunction, and I had managed to translate most of the medical lingo into plain English. "Bilateral axillary lymphadenopathy," for example, meant that the lymph nodes in both armpits were swollen. I guessed that my "shoddy inguinal" nodes meant that the nodes in my groin were of inferior quality. I wondered whose bad idea it was to make the language of medicine so complicated and thought about re-writing Builderese specifically for health care professionals. Imagine the puzzled looks I would get when I asked doctors for their choice of "conflagrated terra" when all I really meant was bricks? I chuckled at the thought of such sweet revenge.

In the dictionary, I looked up alopecia — which in Medicalese means baldness — because I was curious to know its origin. What I didn't expect to learn was that its Greek root, "alopekia," means fox mange. I swear I didn't make that up. As if going bald weren't bad enough, feeling mangy added insult to injury.

For five days straight, my hair vigorously deserted my scalp. Day and night, it rained into the knit cap that I wore. In the garage each morning, I leaned over the garbage can and brushed out clumps, always surprised by how much was left after cutting my hair so short. On the sixth morning, when I brushed what little remained attached to my scalp, the last vestiges stubbornly stayed in place. They were taunting reminders of what had once covered my head. So much for having bad hair days. They'd all be bad for quite some time.

I'd planned to shave what little hair remained that day but decided to wait and see how much more deserted me. None did. The Great Hair Loss was over. I looked in the mirror and thought, "Well, it's official. I look like cancer." And with a few wisps remaining, my head did look mangy. Whoever chose that alopecia word hit the nail on the head, pun intended. Some weeks later, I told Dr. Kaminski that it was a good thing he became a physician because he would have made a lousy hairdresser.

Karen was fascinated by my loss. She wanted to take a picture, but I refused. Mange was outward evidence of my interior malfunction, and I did not need a permanent impression for something that I was struggling to believe was only temporary. Reminders of the normal me was what I needed, and I was turning anywhere I could to find them, including dabbing shampoo on my nearly naked noggin every time I showered. A girl can pretend, can't she?

Mother knew I was losing my hair but still did not associate it with chemotherapy or cancer. She once asked if my blood disorder had a name and I answered that it was called follicular lymphoma. Just as I knew she would, she replied, "Oh, I'll never remember that."

Mother, Karen and I had an enjoyable visit despite the fact that we did nothing of any consequence. Each afternoon, Mother and I invariably dozed, and our only outings were to the hospital for blood tests and to the grocery store. Karen must have been bored out of her wits, but she hid it well.

One evening when Juli called, she spoke with Karen and obviously asked how I was really doing. Karen wandered into another room where she thought I wouldn't hear and told Juli, "Your mother looks like she just got out of Auschwitz." I pretended not to hear, but I wanted to walk into the other room and ask Karen, "When did you say your plane was leaving?" Did I really look that awful? I guess I had thinned down. I'd lost more pounds than Dr. Kaminski's bloat potion had ever put on me, and it would take some time for me to eat enough to regain my normal weight.

As the older sister, Karen could easily have babied me that week. Thankfully, she didn't. She was simply herself and treated me as if nothing were different. While she'd offer to help with dinner, she never insisted on cooking. She must have instinctively known that letting me perform even simple tasks would help me regain my independence and confidence. Big Sister even let me put the dishes in the dishwasher.

Fortunately, Karen watched out for me without smothering me. When I decided to bake a ham at the end of the week, just before Alex was to return, Karen removed it from the oven just after I placed it in. She'd noticed that I'd left the wrapper on it, even while scoring and inserting cloves into it. "Oh gosh," she said lightly. "We were gabbing away and I just noticed this." I felt like a complete idiot, but she laughed it off and sweetly assured me, "We were just paying too much attention to our conversation. Anybody could have done it." No, just someone with the beginning of chemo brain, a side effect that reduces concentration and mental clarity.

Preparing meals for the three of us didn't require much effort. Mother ate little, Karen was content with anything, and my taste buds were beginning to recover, but were nowhere near normal. Throughout their visit, I added a little rice, a little salad and peaches to my diet. And oh, how I devoured sweet, juicy peaches. Except, of course, the two that had served as the landing deck for my hair.

One evening, while I was standing at the kitchen sink peeling peaches, Mother sauntered over, put her hand on my shoulder and said, "You know, peaches are a lot like life. Peel off the unimportant things, throw away the pits, and you have sweet fruit." Hmmm. Such words of wisdom, I thought. Oh, how I desperately wanted to pitch the pits and taste life's sweetness again.

Alex called several times daily, and each day he sounded more and more relaxed. I missed him terribly but was happy that he was taking a well-deserved break from work — and from me and cancer.

Toward the end of the week, he laughed when I warned him to prepare himself for a mangy wife. When I told him that alopecia's root meant fox mange, he replied that I was dwelling on the wrong part of the root. "Forget about the mange. I think you're a fox." I was totally taken aback by this mildly flirtatious response, the first I could remember since my diagnosis. I don't remember what I said, but I do remember thinking that he just hadn't seen me yet and that I wished I could live up to that expectation.

I spent extra time getting ready the morning Alex was due home. I just wanted to look like — be like — my old self. Maybe the wig would help. First I put on the stocking, a wig undergarment which made me look like I was about to rob a bank, and then pulled on the wig which looked, I thought, like bad faux fur. It wasn't a thing like my hair, but it might help me feign resemblance to the old me.

Dressed at last, I went downstairs where Mother and Karen were already getting their breakfast. "You look so cute," they said. "And you can't tell you're wearing a wig." Maybe they couldn't tell, but I could. Even if it had looked exactly like my hair, it felt completely different. Its elastic band gripped my scalp like a vice, and I was quite certain that at any moment it was going to pop straight from the top of my head like a champagne cork. Plus — it itched!

I was as ready as I could be for Alex's homecoming later that morning. Tanned and smiling, he pulled into the driveway a week after he'd left. Thankfully, his hug left no doubt that he had missed me and that his spirit was renewed. Still, I wondered how he would react to my head, so I stripped the wig shortly after his arrival. Without blinking, he pulled me close and said, "You look beautiful." I love it when he lies.

Months later, when I asked him how he had really felt about my naked head, he assured me that he had never cared whether I had hair or not. Hair loss was simply part of the treatment, it was temporary, and it seemed so insignificant compared to what I had gone through in the hospital. "I was just glad you were alive and getting better. I knew your hair would grow back. Your life wouldn't," he said.

Mother and Karen returned to Virginia two days after Alex came home. Never before had I cherished their companionship so deeply. Although my mother's diminished comprehension prevented me from drawing on her emotional strength, I knew that her 92-year-old genes resided in me, and against odds of her own, her continued presence in this world gave me great hope. And that was more encouraging than any words she could have said in her younger years.

I'd expected to return directly home after taking Mother and Karen to the airport, but Judy called while I was on my way home. My neutrophils were down again, and she wanted me to begin taking Neupogen. Would it be possible, she asked, for me to come to the clinic right away? "I'm on my way," I said, wondering all the way there how I would cross the next hurdle.

● ● ●

You gots to work with what you gots to work with.
— Stevie Wonder

12. | BRAIN ON VACATION

Neupogen is a drug which raises the neutrophil count, and I'd have taken anything to avoid another stay in Hotel Hell, but there was a big problem. Neupogen is given by injection — self-injection. How was a yellow-bellied, chicken-hearted milksop like me supposed to jab herself with a razor-sharp instrument? I got light-headed just thinking about it. Maybe it would come with a chaser of smelling salts.

Dr. Kaminski's nurse, Sandy Trembath, would teach me how to administer the shots. When I told her that I had failed masochist school, she promised to give them to me herself if I couldn't. I loved her for giving me that safety net, but I agreed to try.

I watched a video about Neupogen and self-injections — three times. Each time, I followed the instructions, pinching my thigh in preparation for the poke and using my fingernail to pretend it was puncturing the skin. And each time, my tummy turned somersaults, and my eyes involuntarily turned away before penetration — and this was only pretend!

At the end of the video, the spokesman said, "Congratulations for participating in your care." She sounded so smug that I retorted in frustration, "I'm not going to participate in this particular part of my care. What are you gonna do about it, lady?"

I knew what I was going to do about it. I called Alex, asked if he would lend his bravery to a worthy cause, and he reluctantly promised to try. I knew that he was a little squeamish about shots, but since he'd once planned to become a surgeon, I assumed that he knew that he would have had to inflict gruesome gashes, far more invasive than those needles — which were, in truth, miniscule.

Sandy gave me the shot that day. Alex and I returned the following afternoon for his lesson, but when she handed him the syringe, every bit of color drained from his face as he involuntarily stepped back. Clearly, he was no better at shooting me up than I was. I promised Sandy we could find people to give me the shots, and she never made us feel like the sissies we were.

On the way home, Alex looked disappointed, and he finally admitted, "I'm afraid I'll hurt you." Touched by his tenderness, I tried to assure him that giving shots was hard for many people, that it wasn't necessary for him to do everything for me, and that he shouldn't be embarrassed or disappointed. Our friend Marie the dentist gave me the injections for the remainder of the week, and she never made fun of Alex or me.

For the next couple of months, blood was extracted twice a week by some of the sweetest nurses I have ever met. They were well aware that their cancer patients were in serious medical trouble, but their smiles, their friendly manners, and their encouraging words maintained a positive, upbeat atmosphere in the blood drawing area. Most importantly, those internal audits kept Dr. Kaminski, Judy and me well informed in case my blood decided to entertain any diabolical acts. And how badly could it damage me between those frequent audits?

Despite taking Neupogen and the regular blood draws, I became pre-occupied with infection and feared that my body was defenseless against relentlessly attacking germs which might send me straight back to Hotel Hell. I learned a dozen ways or more to avoid infection — just what I always wanted to know. I avoided crowds and washed my hands constantly, fearing that germs were crawling all over them. When I couldn't wash them, I used antibacterial wipes. Tasting germs in every bite, I washed food until it was barely recognizable, even before cooking it. We stopped going to restaurants for fear that germs lurked in their kitchens. On the handles of grocery carts, on my steering wheel, on doorknobs, I imagined a microscopic army plotting to invade my body. Germs were everywhere, and they made life itself a danger. I became a virtual exile, preferring to stay at home unless it was absolutely necessary to go out.

Fortunately, I could work mostly at home and by phone. By early July, when the third CHOP and the second Rituxan treatment were administered on the same day, I was tired, but could stay awake throughout almost every day. But by that time, a good part of my brain had packed up and gone on vacation. What stayed behind could barely remember the simplest things.

Still, I really did want to work, and Alex encouraged me to do as much as I felt I could. I'd schedule meetings with clients or prospective clients, and I found it uncanny that, on one pretense or another, he just happened to drop by during my meetings. It would take me months to figure out that he was giving me just enough room to regain my confidence without giving me any room to fall flat on my face. Pretty good guy, huh?

In truth, I was barely competent. I couldn't remember our building contracts, which at one time I knew backward and forward. When prospective clients asked about change orders, I fumbled through the pages looking for the appropriate paragraph instead of reciting the contract language while referring them to Paragraph 14, Page 3. And I could barely calculate the math regardless of how simple it was. A $500,000 purchase with a $100,000 deposit left what balance? I would stare at the numbers and eventually use a calculator to figure it out.

My attempts at client selections were worse. Our purchasing agent ordered all materials directly from selection forms, and I had always been extremely careful to submit them accurately. One transposed number could mean very unhappy clients if pink carpet were installed instead of beige. When I submitted a selection form with two different tiles for the same fireplace, we all realized that my remaining brain cells should be added to the endangered species list. Alex began to double check all my work.

With housing inventory up that summer, I should have been proactively marketing our properties more aggressively than ever, but I rarely gave it a thought. Even when I did try to develop marketing materials, I would sit staring at the computer for hours, drawing a complete blank. Not good for someone who had once been able to write marketing materials effortlessly.

And oblivious to time, deadlines for selections came and went, and I simply forgot that the office needed to purchase materials by specific dates in order to maintain the flow of construction. Although Alex had no spare time to tackle one more task, he somehow picked up that slack, too, although I was relatively unaware of it at the time.

I am very lucky than neither our purchasing agent nor Alex was ever critical, at least not to my face. Of course they were both in awkward positions. How could Alex replace his wife in the middle of her battle with cancer? And how could an employee criticize the boss's wife? I'm sure their patience stretched awfully thin sometimes.

Much later, Alex admitted that my diminished mental faculties did frustrate him at times and that occasionally he had to remind himself that chemo brain was only a temporary side effect. "Mostly," he said, "I saw your efforts and interest as an encouraging sign of your determination to maintain a normal life. And if you made a few mistakes or were a little too slow along the way, I much preferred your making attempts to making none at all."

Alex also told me that I had asked him for help on a number of occasions and that he had thought that I must be improving if I could recognize my own fogginess. Funny, I don't remember asking him for a single thing.

In early July, our lumber salesman died of liver cancer. He'd been diagnosed just six weeks earlier, and his quick death frightened me. His funeral scared the hell out of me. Getting dressed for it, I collapsed on the floor of our closet, sobbing. Just when I'd started to regain some hope, this reminder of death snatched it away. Not only that, making myself presentable seemed like an insurmountable challenge. The wig was too unbearably hot, and I wasn't about to expose my mangy head. I finally settled on a dress with a matching hat and was the only person at the service wearing a head covering — which only magnified how different I was from everyone else.

On the way home, Alex and I stopped at the hardware store where an older gentleman said to me, "Excuse me, but I couldn't help but notice your hat. It's lovely, and you don't often see such elegance these days."

I have no idea how I responded to that man. I hope I thanked him, but chemo may very well have destroyed my etiquette cells. It didn't destroy my anger. In the car moments later, I burst into tears and sobbed, "I hate this hat. If my body hadn't betrayed me, I wouldn't be wearing it."

Startled, Alex tried to help me look at the brighter side. "Betsy, the compliment should make you happy. You look great today, and you're hiding the illness well."

"I don't want to hide anything," I wept inconsolably, "and I don't want to be sick."

That night, I asked Alex if he would promise to cremate me. He furrowed his eyebrows and sighed, "Betsy, you're going to be around for a long time. You shouldn't worry yourself about that."

"I'm not worried. Just promise you'll burn me," I said.

His face contorted as he replied, "Betsy, I don't even want to talk about this. And why do you have to be so blunt?"

"Well, talking about it isn't going to kill either of us. And burning's what it is. So please just promise."

Alex finally shut me up by saying, "I think you'll outlive me. But if you promise to cremate me, I'll cremate you if anything happens

to you first." We had a deal. It was the first time we had mentioned
the possibility of death, at least that I remembered, and I knew when
to stop. I didn't dare ask him to scatter my ashes in the ocean, but I
did wonder if he was in complete denial that I might actually die.

From that day forward and for the next several weeks, my car
and I detoured whenever I drove to our downtown office, which I
occasionally visited for various reasons. The most direct route took
me directly past Muehlig Funeral Chapel where Dan's funeral had
been held, but I could no longer drive past the place without envi-
sioning my remains in some little urn. It wasn't that I feared death.
I just wasn't ready to die. And so I began taking a different route to
the office, as if I could avoid the urn by avoiding the building.

By mid-July, just prior to the fourth CHOP and third Rituxan
treatment, Alex and I were thrilled that another CT scan indicated
that the toxins were winning at last. I began to allow myself to think
— a little — about life after chemo. Maybe, just maybe, I would
someday return to the Land of the Healthy.

Alex and I celebrated by taking a day trip. We packed a cooler
and drove north, stopping at a beach and wading along the shore of
Lake Huron. I had longed to be in Florida with Juli and the babies,
but didn't dare set foot in a germ-infested airplane. I had longed,
too, for the ocean, but had satisfied that desire by holding a conch
shell to my ear and pretending that the waves were lapping at my
feet. Lake Huron was as close as I was going to get to any large body
of water that summer, and I giggled with delight when I wiggled my
toes in the water. And I was happy that the weather was unusually
hot that day. Similar to Florida's, I was grateful for any reminder of
where I wanted to be.

We nearly left cancer in Ann Arbor for the entire day, referring
to it only once when I told Alex that I wanted to leave something
permanent for the people I love. Should I paint something special
for him? Write a poem? What would he like? His face told me that
he wished I hadn't brought up any reference to my possible demise,

but without hesitation he said, "You already gave me something permanent. My wedding ring."

This wasn't a typical wedding ring. It was a signet ring emblazoned with his family's coat-of-arms. For years, I'd heard about a similar ring which had belonged to his father and which had been stolen during a robbery in Alex's house shortly after Ted had given it to him some twenty-five or so years earlier. I'd never known Alex to wear jewelry, not even a watch, but that ring was obviously sentimental to him. I'd gone to great lengths to have another made, inscribed with our wedding date, and had surprised him with it during our wedding ceremony. I'd never really expected him to wear it, but from that day forward, he'd never taken it off.

I was happy that the ring meant so much to him and made no further reference to cancer or its potential doom that day. Smiling, I laid my head against the seat and rolled the window down, inviting the hot air to caress my face. I felt — *alive!*

● ● ●

Friendship isn't about whom you've known the longest but
who came and never left your side.
— Author Unknown

13. | DO'S AND DON'TS

In late July, I looked forward to spending an evening with three couples who had volunteered to bring dinner. As we were setting the food out buffet style, my friend Oksana asked how I was doing. "Fine," I answered.

"But how are you really doing?" she pressed. "I mean, are you coping okay?"

"I suppose I am," I answered, and then joked, "If my life were on TV, 'Stand by: we're experiencing temporary difficulties' would be stuck on the screen."

Oksana chuckled and then asked, "Has losing your hair been hard for you?"

"Well," I began, "I don't like losing my hair, but there are bigger fish to fry at the moment. I think the hardest thing about it is that it reminds me of my illness and makes me feel different. If I just looked like everybody else, then maybe I could feel like everybody else."

Oksana then asked, "May I go upstairs for a minute?" It sounded like an odd response, but I said, "Of course."

In minutes, she returned with my hats and scarves and began to hand them out to everyone. Alex chose the wide-brimmed purple straw hat. Pavlo selected a pink scarf. And so it went, amidst much laughter, until all heads were covered. Oksana then turned to me and said, "Now we're all alike." Everyone kept their hats on for the duration of the evening, and I couldn't help but giggle at the motley hat brigade whose antics showed so much love and support.

Throughout the summer, and in fact throughout my illness, I was very grateful that friends and acquaintances kept in touch. Sometimes I was too tired to talk, but a message on the answering machine meant that someone cared. Cards, phone calls and emails were humbling reminders that I mattered enough for others to take the time to think about me, but given my state of mind, words sometimes hurt more than they helped, however well-intentioned they might have been.

I'd never known what to say to someone who had cancer, so I didn't expect my family or friends to know any better than I did, but the platitudes got old. Maybe we cancer patients should come with a manual — one that would be required reading of do's and don'ts for families and friends before they open their mouths. This is what mine would have said:

You ask how I feel and most of the time I say fine. Indeed, having cancer and going through treatment has made me FINE — feeling insecure, nervous and emotional — so it's no wonder that you may not recognize me as the person you know or love. To tell you the truth, some days I don't recognize me, either, and I'm not sure I'd know what to say to me if I were you. All I can tell you is that some days I want to talk about my illness. Other days, I don't. Most days, I don't know what I want. How, then, could you? Yet most of you are trying so hard to make me feel better, and I appreciate that. I also wish that I could make it easier for you. Maybe this will help.

Rest assured that there are no "right" words for every cancer patient. Our illnesses, situations and personalities are unique, but I'm pretty sure that our collective sensitivity is heightened, and there are definitely some things that should never be said, at least to me. For instance:

Please don't tell me that if I have to have cancer, this is a good one to get. Let's not sugar coat this. There's no such thing as Cancer Lite. And please don't give me statistics. I am not a number.

Please don't tell me that you know what I'm going through. How could you? Instead, let me know that you can't walk in my shoes but that you will always walk beside me.

Please don't ask me if there's anything you can do. I probably won't tell you, not because I'm being stubborn but because most of the time, I just don't know. Instead, make me an offer I can't refuse. And if you ask open-ended questions, it's likely you'll succeed in really helping me carry this weight. Example: "I'm bringing you dinner. Would Tuesday or Thursday be better?" But please don't do this unless you mean it and plan to follow through because if I count on you to do what you say and you don't, you'll make my life even worse.

Please don't tell me how "lucky" I am that so many advances have been made. Would you feel "lucky" to have cancer?

Please don't minimize my feelings by telling me not to worry or that I'll be fine or that I can beat this. Try having cancer and not worrying. And how do you know that I'll be fine or that I can beat it? What life has in store for us doesn't always correlate to our will or effort. And what if I don't beat it? Will it be my fault? Instead, tell me that you hope I hear good news at my next appointment. Or commiserate by saying, "What a lousy thing you're going through." At least then I would know that you respect my feelings.

Please don't tell me that I just have to think positive. Sometimes the only thing I'm positive about is that I have cancer, and it stinks. And excuse me, but my attitude neither caused my cancer nor can it cure it, and thinking positive all the time is neither realistic nor sustainable. Sure, a good attitude helps me slog through chemotherapy, but sometimes I need to cry. It doesn't mean I'm giving up. It just means I'm human. You'd let me bawl if my cat died. And you wouldn't tell me to think positive if I fell off my bike and broke my arm. Why is cancer different?

Please don't tell me how brave I am. If I'd volunteered to have cancer for you, that might have been brave. Frankly, I'd rather be sucking my thumb. Instead, make me laugh. You can always send me jokes by email.

Please don't tell me that any one of us could get hit by a bus tomorrow. Cancer happens in epic proportions. More than a million and half Americans are diagnosed every year, and that's far more perilous than crossing the street.

Please don't tell me how great I look. Would you think you look great with no hair, no eyebrows, no lashes? If you insist on paying me a compliment, make it an honest one, such as "Hey, I like your blouse" or "Your cheeks have more color this week."

Please don't ask me how it feels to be bald. How would you feel? Instead, try telling me, "I love you with or without hair." But only if you mean it.

Please don't tell me about your Aunt Sally or Uncle Charlie who had this or that kind of cancer. They have nothing to do with me. Instead, you might offer to help me find accurate information, from reliable sources, about my kind of cancer. Better yet, bring over a good movie and watch it with me. Funny ones are the best kinds because the power of laughter can't be overstated.

Please don't tell me how worried you are about me. I don't need the additional responsibility of cheering you up.

Sometimes, the best words are, "I'm not sure what to say, but I love you no matter what." And sometimes no words are necessary when a simple hug will do. Most of you already know that. You aren't the ones who sent one card and then disappeared, as if mortality is contagious and coming into contact with me makes you susceptible. You are the ones who've joined me for the long haul, sometimes putting your own lives on hold — not because you have to, but because you want to. I love you for that, especially because I know that loving or befriending a cancer patient means, at times, that you feel sad, frightened, angry, lonely and helpless.

But helpless you're not. Each one of you is a connection to my life before cancer, and your love and friendship gives me hope for life after cancer. You give me reason and strength to carry on when I feel like giving up. No one can do this for me but you, and I have never needed or appreciated your love and friendship more.

● ● ●

Most people really were wonderful, but a few disappeared. One day I ran into one of our former clients who nervously apologized for not calling. "I just can't handle illness," he said. "It makes me think I'll die." I almost laughed and asked, "So what makes you think you won't?" At least he was honest about it. The fact is, cancer shoves death in people's faces, and some friends become strangers. But some strangers become friends.

There would be one other note in a manual that I would give to family and friends: please remember the caregiver. Alex's pain and fear were often overlooked, yet he had the much more difficult task of juggling work while trying to cope, often helplessly and always without training, with my illness and its potential ramifications. I always wished that someone — anyone — would send a card to Alex and Alex only or simply take him out and buy him a beer to get him away from me. No one ever did, but any gesture that would have recognized his role would have meant the world to me.

He was, after all, going through hell. Not only was he playing Head Cheerleader, but he would make dinner when he came home and found me asleep. He would vacuum when I was too tired. He would chauffeur me to tests and appointments. And he had already taken on much of my job. In addition to all that, there were the normal challenges of work. Up until then, our clients had been delightful. In fact, many had become friends. But suddenly we had two of the most demanding situations we'd had in our careers. When it rains, it pours.

One of those situations began the previous December. We had just dug the foundation for a home when our clients decided to divorce. Lest building a home take the blame, it was the direct result of a cheatin' heart — which apparently wasn't the only cheating body part. We were peripherally drawn into the fray when Mr. and Mrs. Divorce stopped making payments on their construction loan. Consequently, we stopped getting paid. I offered to help them sell their hole in the ground, free of charge, only to have Mr. Divorce, himself a cancer survivor, tell me rudely and emphatically that he didn't think I could handle it — given my circumstances and all. I guess even cancer survivors can sometimes be jerks. We ultimately did get rid of their house problem for them, although it was neither pleasant nor profitable.

Another couple, with whom we'd signed a contract just before my diagnosis, made it clear from the beginning that they were going to be the most difficult clients we'd ever had, bar none. I'd never wanted to build for them in the first place because I thought they were unhappy people with bad attitudes, but Alex was willing to give them the benefit of the doubt. That's probably because we'd never had clients from hell before.

From the get-go, they were like kids who pit parents against each other. Alex said this, they would tell me, and Betsy said that, they would tell him. It was all an effort to get whatever they could. Once chemo began, Alex and I agreed that I should bow out, figuring that they couldn't pit him against himself. But that didn't stop the problems. Far from it. They wouldn't make selections on time so we couldn't order materials without knowing, for example, what color roof shingles or cabinet styles they wanted. Additionally, changes were made to changes, sometimes after things were installed. And when construction fell behind schedule, they blamed Alex. They also tried to get items at no cost through various and sundry untruthful and sneaky methods, including trying to charge items to our accounts at our suppliers. A couple of costly items did slip through the cracks, and I asked Alex, after he had finally finished the house late in the year, why he had let that happen. He sighed deeply, his shoulders sagged, and he looked so weary that I thought he was going to cry when he answered, "Betsy, this year has been hell. How many battles can I fight?" I felt horrible.

Alex never could get this couple to understand their role in the process or that their cooperation was crucial. Maybe that's because some people thrive on their own misery, but whatever it was, this couple is the perfect example of what not to do in any relationship. Whether it's with a builder or a medical team, cooperation is always a two-way street and there's no point in making any process any harder than it has to be.

Our other clients were truly wonderful. They knew that I was a little busy with cancer, and they went out of their way to make choices on time and sometimes rescheduled their own busy lives so that meetings were convenient for Alex and me. Months later, when I lightly and apologetically made fun of my chemo brain, all were surprised that I even had it. At first I thought I had concealed it better than I had remembered, but when I reviewed my journal as well as my files, I realized that Alex had almost always been around for every meeting I had.

Despite trying to work and maintain a regular routine, I felt drained and vulnerable, but my brain was still functioning enough to know that I could weave an emotional safety net by making some conscious choices. And I did — about what I read, what I watched, how I ate, how I exercised. And those choices — do's and don'ts for myself — not only helped to remind me that I hadn't completely lost control of my life, but, in retrospect, they also influenced how I responded to illness.

For starters, I quit watching the news, which ordinarily Alex and I regularly read and watched, but it had grown increasingly disturbing, full as it seemed to be of horrors of one group or person slaying another. Fighting for my own life, I was distressed by any unnecessary death and confounded by anyone who would sacrifice life for political ideology or any other reason. The solution was simple: shut it down.

Instead of the news, I watched funny movies and re-runs of *I Love Lucy* and *M*A*S*H* or anything else that would buffer the grim reality of worldly conflicts or my lymphoma. I searched for stories about long shot victories. They were inspirational and reassuring as I dreamed of a victory of my own. And if I missed news about interest rates, I rationalized that somebody would fill me in.

Sometimes I read medical studies, but always, those disturbing statistics stood out. As hard as it sometimes was, Alex and I tried to forget them. Statistics are only numbers, and we kept telling ourselves that numbers couldn't kill me. That statistics define large groups of people, but not me individually.

And each day, we consciously tried to find something, however small, for which to be thankful. Some days it was hard to find anything, but searching for positives helped to offset the negatives. I'd even started a "Things I Am Thankful For" list. Especially on the days when I would rather have been wallowing in self-pity, I forced myself to add something to the list, and something on it always made me smile. Aside from family and friends, a few things on it were Hershey kisses, sunshine, sunsets, thunderstorms, Key lime pie, anti-nausea drugs, old family photographs, life's little conveniences like dishwashers and covered parking when it's snowing, my favorite pair of purple heels and instant-dry nail polish.

Yes, I'd come up with some self-soothing solutions to buoy my spirits, but there was one thing I couldn't solve that drove me crazy, and that was when people thought that lymphoma was a virus. At least I had known that it was a type of cancer when I was diagnosed, and it annoyed me that everyone seemed to know about various other types of cancers that were attached to the "C" word.

I'd learned that, collectively, the blood cancers — leukemia, lymphoma and myeloma — were the third leading cause of death among the cancers (behind lung and colon cancer) and that the incidence of lymphoma had doubled since the 1970's. How could people *not* know about the blood cancers? Even with chemo brain fogging my mind, I still noticed that pink was the only ribbon on various products, and I was beginning to suspect that there was not only a hierarchy in the world of cancer but that certain ones had pedigrees. I bitterly complained to Alex that awareness of the blood cancers must be raised. He would then challenge me to get well and do something about it, as if I could.

In early August, a downtown theater was showing *Sunshine State*, an offbeat comedy about out-of-state developers trying to buy a small Florida town. I'd seen enough developers try to buy chunks of Florida to know that I would love the movie, but Alex and I were concerned about going to a public place where some stranger might sneeze. We decided we'd go during the week when fewer people might infect me. I could hardly wait for our date.

As we walked into the theater, I headed straight for the concession stand for popcorn and a Coke. Alex, always my Great Protector, gently suggested, "Betsy, we may be pushing it already. Don't you think you should skip this?"

"Absolutely not," I replied. "When's the last time we went out? Let's have a little fun."

Alex reminded me that we could have lots of fun without popcorn which might have germs that could hurt me. "Why don't you just have the Coke?" he asked.

"My dear," I laughed, "I feel like being very naughty. Oooooooo — we're out in a public place. I'm about to have popcorn smothered in butter. And if you're a good boy, I'll share it with you." Alex knew then that the popcorn was non-negotiable, so he smiled, shook his head and kissed my cheek.

For two hours during that movie, I felt like a normal human being. We enjoyed every morsel of popcorn and laughed at the one-liners about developers who tried, unsuccessfully, to gobble up Florida real estate. We were still laughing as we walked arm-in-arm to the car. In the parking garage, I skipped circles around Alex, wanting the evening to last forever. That and our day trip were the highlights of my entire summer, which I spent mostly in oblivion, thanks to the vacation that most of my brain was taking.

Frankly, I'm uncertain how I spent most days, and they often passed without my knowing — or caring — whether it was Tuesday or Friday. I knew Sundays, though, because Ted and Lisa always brought dinner so that we wouldn't have to cook, and Greta and Zan usually joined us. It was the one stable routine that I could count on.

Most days, I was too tired even to hold a paperback, and reading sent me to slumberland after a few pages anyway. Gardening was off limits because spores in the dirt could cause infection. I know that I spent many hours successfully teaching my constant companion — our cat — to play catch. Never, not once, did I ever feel nauseated. And I marveled at other patients who were going through chemotherapy and who seemed to be living their lives far more normally than I.

Mostly, my mind and body just seemed to be idling that summer. Some days were good. Some were bad. Sometimes I needed to talk about my illness. Sometimes I didn't. Most of the time, I didn't know what I wanted. How then could anyone else?

Alex and I were happy that I had stayed out of Hotel Hell and that all signs indicated that the drugs were doing their job. And then, on Saturday morning, August 10, two days before the sixth treatment was scheduled, I awoke with a fever. Could there really have been germs in that popcorn?

● ● ●

When you're at the end of your rope, tie a knot and hang on.
— *Franklin D. Roosevelt*

14. | CELLS GO WILD AGAIN

Hot flashes flashed and fever brewed. I knew the symptoms all too well. Lymphoma was back, raging furiously. Several times I blinked back tears, not knowing how to break the news to Alex. I didn't that day. I spent most of it on the couch wondering what in the world we were going to do. How much more could he take? And how much more could I?

Visions of my father popped into my head without warning, and that night, I saw his face in one dream after another. He was silent, but I feared that I was in grave danger of joining him.

I woke up angry that my cancer cells were so intent on outsmarting chemo. I told myself that if I ignored the fever, it would disappear if I just did something normal. And so on that Sunday morning, I dragged out the vacuum cleaner and with gritted teeth and a fever of 101, I vacuumed the house as if to suck up every danger that surrounded me. Real normal, huh?

Alex wandered into our bedroom, where I finally turned off the vacuum, and asked if I was feeling okay. "I'm just fine," I announced defiantly through still gritted teeth. And with that, I burst into tears, jumped back into our unmade bed, curled up into a fetal position, and pulled the covers over my head, hoping to find safety from fever and cancer and even death. How's that for coping skills?

Alex sat on the edge of our bed and slowly pulled the covers from my head. "What's going on?" he asked. I was sobbing so hard that I could barely tell him that I was running a fever, my father wouldn't leave me alone, and I was sure that lymphoma was back.

"I-I-I-I'm a-a-a-afraid I-I-I-I'm g-g-g-gonna d-d-d-die," I wailed.

Ever positive, Alex did his best to remind me that the recent CT scan had shown that chemo was doing its job. My father was just trying to let me know that he'll always watch over me. And the fever? The books, and Dr. Kaminski, said that fever could occur for many reasons. Wasn't I getting myself too worked up when there could be other explanations? No, I wasn't. I knew that chemo had done a better job at knocking out my hair than my cancer, and I was filled with terror.

Alex tried so hard and so gently to comfort me, to convince me to keep my mind open to other explanations, and to keep hope alive. But no matter what he said, I could only sob deep, sorrowful, body-shaking sobs, and all Alex could do was stroke my head and hand me tissues. Lots of tissues.

When I finally quit soaking my pillow, we called the hospital. Within minutes, Dr. Kaminski returned the call and, like Alex, assured me that there could be many explanations. Since I was scheduled to see him the following morning prior to the next chemo treatment, he suggested that we stay put, unless the fever rose, and then I was to head to the emergency room. Dr. Kaminski always had a soothing effect on me, and I was willing to hope that this was anything but another attack of lymphoma. So was Alex.

But hope was one thing. Reality was another, and I could not ignore the symptoms that were threatening my life. In my angst, I decided to sort through some family items and mark them well. I began with some jewelry that had belonged to my grandmothers, placing the pieces in small boxes and identifying the original owners, not sure if Juli would remember. I placed the boxes in Ziploc bags and put them in one of my dresser drawers. And then I showed

Alex what I had accomplished and asked him please to give the bags to Juli when I was dead and gone.

Horrified, he asked, "Betsy, what are you doing this for?"

"I want to make it easier for everybody," I answered matter-of-factly. Alex pulled me close and begged me to think of living, not dying. And just how was I supposed to ignore that distinct possibility with fever and hot flashes raging again?

By late afternoon the fever spiked to 103. Following Dr. Kaminski's instructions, Alex and I headed for the emergency room where the doctor checked for pneumonia. Happy to hear any possible reason other than lymphoma, I scoffed, "What's wrong with this picture? We're glad I might have pneumonia?" Alex and I chuckled at how our perspectives had changed during the year. We didn't chuckle when the X-ray was clear.

In the emergency room, my hopes lifted. Maybe I was overreacting. Maybe I was plain paranoid. But by the time we arrived home close to midnight, I was convinced that the disease had returned. The symptoms were all too familiar, and that's exactly what I told Dr. Kaminski and Judy the following morning, much to Alex's chagrin. There I was, losing hope again, he feared.

Always the optimist, Dr. Kaminski tried to reassure us that we couldn't be certain without tests to confirm, but — for the first time since I'd known them — I was sure that his and Judy's eyes looked worried, and I made some sarcastic remark like "You can do all the tests you want, but you and I both know it's back." Graciously ignoring my sarcasm, he said we would have the tests and make a determination when we had the results. And he reminded me that we still had options. There were other chemotherapies, radioimmunotherapy, and just in case, we should type Karen's and my blood to learn if she would be a suitable donor if we needed a bone marrow transplant.

Whoa. A bone marrow transplant? I wasn't ready to think about that, much less discuss it. At our first meeting with Dr. Kaminski, I recalled that a bone marrow transplant was the last treatment he mentioned. He had thoroughly explained all the others, but said that he didn't want to go into the details of a transplant at that time, adding that it was the last option. I also knew that a transplant was risky. Now, seven months later, that last option was reintroduced as a possibility. Was I at the end of the line already? Dr. Kaminski sensed my panic, assured me that we simply needed to be ready if necessary and that we had a long way to go before a transplant.

I loved the way Dr. Kaminski and Judy — and in fact all their colleagues — said *we*. Sometimes it almost made me laugh, like when they said "*We* will have a CT scan." I came close to asking if they meant we'd have a group picture, all of us lying together on the narrow slab and sliding through the machine. Humor aside, their choice of this simple, small word implied that they were treating me as their partner, when in fact I always saw Dr. Kaminski as the commander-in-chief, Judy as his adjutant and myself as merely an unwilling draftee.

"We" did not have chemotherapy that day. Instead, Dr. Kaminski prescribed Decadron, a steroid which reduces fever, can kill malignant lymphocytes, and causes insomnia. That's an understatement. Within days, I was sleeping about two hours a night and jittering as if I'd consumed 500 cups of coffee when I was awake, which further scrambled my brain and emotions. Industrial strength No-Doz was merely a stopgap measure until "we" determined the future course of action which would depend on the results of another CT scan and bone marrow biopsy, both scheduled for the following day.

I should have dreaded the biopsy or taken more Versed because I remembered every single tap-tap-tap of that needle, and it hurt. I liked the CT scan much better. No muss. No fuss. No needles.

I was asleep that evening when Juli called, and I would later learn that Alex told her we were running out of options. I'd planned to fly down the second I finished chemo, but this latest complication made my travel plans very uncertain. Juli promised to come up to see me, a big step for someone who absolutely hates to fly.

Wednesday morning arrived, and leaving "our" options to Dr. Kaminski, I considered what I should do. Since my body seemed so determined to kill me, it occurred to me that I should write my obituary. Left to Alex, he might simply say, "Betsy died." Oh, how very eloquent. But how do you write your own obituary? I abandoned the idea. Should I at least plan a funeral? Choose the music? I smirked as I thought that "Stayin' Alive" would be a little late. And just why was I dwelling on my own demise? I was thrilled that my daughter and grandbabies were coming, and surely Dr. Kaminski would come up with something.

Later that day, he called with results. The tests proved what I already knew. Lymphoma was back — again. The charts would say that I had failed CVP and CHOP with Rituxan. No, they failed me. If anything was going to stop my stubborn disease, it would have to attack the cancer differently than chemo. So what was the back-up plan?

"Betsy, I've made all the arrangements for you to take Zevalin. You'll have to go to another clinic because we're not set up to give it. I've already talked to the doctors there and you have an appointment next Monday." Whoa, Dr. Kaminski. You did what? You transferred me and my cancer cells to another hospital? To take Zevalin? Your very own Bexxar's rival?

I knew about Zevalin. It was the direct competitor of Dr. Kaminski's Bexxar, the drug he had spent years developing and which was still under FDA review. Both drugs belong to a class of medicine known as radioimmunotherapy (RIT), and they attack certain types of lymphoma with laser-like precision. Antibodies seek, find and attach to a particular protein (CD20) found on the surface of B-cell lymphomas. This recruits the immune system to destroy them. For a dual-action and extra lethal effect, radiolabeled antibodies then deliver a minute dose of radiation. This has the effect of destroying malignant cells while mostly sparing healthy ones, which means far fewer side effects. Put another way, RIT acts like a guided missile, precisely homing in on the target, while chemotherapy is more like buckshot, hitting everything in its way, from healthy to malignant cells — or in my case, missing by a mile.

Also unlike chemotherapy, which as I had learned takes several grueling months, RIT is given in two doses a week apart. Better yet, the results in clinical trials had shown great success.

My very own Dr. Kaminski, along with his colleague, Dr. Richard Wahl, a nuclear medicine physician, had perfected the theory of radioimmunotherapy. In 1990, they opened their first clinical trial to patients and steak-sized tumors disappeared within days. Eventually, their treatment became known as Bexxar.

In the medical world, news like this travels fast. Another drug company later began work on its own version of RIT and it became known as Zevalin. In a neck and neck race to bring the two drugs to market, Zevalin received accelerated approval by the FDA in February 2002. I didn't get it. Bexxar had been studied on more patients — and longer.

I had been closely watching this race and had hoped that Bexxar would be approved in case I needed it. I was, after all, Dr. Kaminski's patient, and if I needed RIT, I certainly wanted to take his drug, but all the Bexxar clinical trials which would fit my situation were closed. Alas, it was impossible for me to become a Bexxar Babe.

Zevalin was my only option, but I couldn't understand why the FDA approved it based on shorter studies and fewer patients than Bexxar. Once again, Dr. Kaminski came to my rescue. As a leading expert on RIT, and thoroughly familiar with the differences between Bexxar and Zevalin, he was confident that Zevalin was a reasonable choice. And I was confident in him.

But I was also doing what we patients do to our oncologists: loyally holding on to him for dear life. After Dr. Kaminski and I said goodbye, I pondered this development for several long minutes. Chemo brain and complete exhaustion were the perfect recipe to blind me to the big picture — like saving my life. I decided that since Dr. Kaminski had spent his career developing a drug to save lymphoma patients, and together with his colleagues had fought every battle with me, I was going to be his success if I was going to be anyone's. No one else's. Period. Non-negotiable.

I called Alex and shared the news. He was so thankful that Dr. Kaminski had made all the necessary arrangements — and so quickly. And then I told him that I was going to wait for Bexxar's approval because I wanted to be Dr. Kaminski's success. Alex let out a huge sigh. He clearly saw the bigger picture and finally asked, "How could you possibly be his success if you refuse the very drug that may save your life?"

We debated for awhile until I finally saw the light. "Okay, so I was just having a blonde moment," I quipped.

"No excuses. You don't have any blonde anymore," Alex teased, no doubt breathing a sigh of relief. I chuckled and suddenly realized that Dr. Kaminski clearly didn't care who got the credit for getting me well. His ego never came into play. My wellness was his only concern. And that's a sign of a great doctor and human being.

But I would have to leave him and his colleagues to take Zevalin. Believing that Bexxar's approval was imminent, U of M had not, at the time, become licensed to administer Zevalin. I'd have to go to another hospital and another clinic. Dread stabbed at me. All my old fears about the health care system resurfaced. There would be a whole new group of people who would be clueless about me and my life, and then more than ever I needed the familiarity of the people I knew and trusted.

"I hate the FDA for expelling me from my own U of M sanctuary," I whined to Alex. "What's wrong with those people?"

Alex would have preferred to stay at U of M as well, but always more rational than I, he saw that it wasn't an option. Reminding me of the success of RIT, he would say, "Try to forget about everything else and focus on the outcome." Easy for you to say, I thought.

At the end of that week, Judy called to ask how I was feeling. I told her I was feeling fine, but she knew better. The real reason for her call was to assure me that she and Dr. Kaminski were not abandoning me. "We'll always be here for you," she said so sweetly that I almost cried. Her call was one of many that had buoyed my spirits throughout my illness.

Later in the day I told Alex about Judy's call. "She's not just a nurse. She's a saint," I said, "*and* chief angel on this earth. Every doctor should have a Judy." Alex agreed, thinking to himself that every kindness she — or anyone — had extended to me had also given him a brief reprieve from playing Head Cheerleader.

On Monday, August 20, Alex took me and my cancer cells to the new clinic where the new doctor talked about refractory lymphoma and Zevalin. He reminded us that chemo-resistant lymphoma is not a good sign. Great, tell us something we don't know. By now, he said, Zevalin had been administered to about 800, maybe 1,000 patients, and it was so new that there were no studies available to indicate its long-term effectiveness, especially on patients who had failed chemo. I wanted to scream back, "I didn't fail chemo. It failed me." Then he added that I'd be lucky for it to hold my lymphoma in check for ten months. He suggested that I talk with the Bone Marrow Transplant unit at U of M as soon as possible.

Although this new doctor was nice enough, his words and his body language clearly conveyed, "There's not a lot of hope for you." Fragile as I was, this message only magnified my fears and frustrations. Looking back, he didn't listen to his own words: no studies are available to indicate its long-term effectiveness. That was a fact, and there is where he should have stopped. Adding that I might be dead in ten months, which is what I heard, Dr. Doom dampened every hope I had.

Walking to the car after our meeting, I once again buried my head in Alex's shoulder and sobbed, "Ten months? Why bother? And then what? A bone marrow transplant? You mean the same thing that killed King Hussein? No thanks. I won't do it."

Alex stopped walking, put one hand on each of my shoulders, turned to me and said with as much authority in his voice as he could muster, "Betsy, remember that Dr. Kaminski has been studying these drugs for years. He's a scientist, a researcher, as well as a physician. No wonder he's comfortable with them. You can't let a few words get you down.'"

Hearing little, my eyes widened as they always do when I try to make a point, and I replied sadly, "Alex, if you think ten days in the hospital was hard, you ain't seen nothin'. I've read a little about transplants and I don't want to put you — or me — through it. I can't. It's that simple." My chin was quivering hard when I looked straight into his eyes and added, "If all I have left is a few months, then can't we just make the most of them without a bunch of horrible treatments? Can't we just go off and be happy?"

There in the parking lot, Alex threw his head back and sighed, not knowing what else to say. He drew me close to him, held me tenderly, and ran one hand through the faux fur. Chuckling through my tears, I whimpered, "Don't even think about pulling my wig off."

Drawing me even closer, he gently whispered back, "I promise I won't if you'll promise to keep all your options open."

With our arms still around each other, I pushed away from his shoulder, looked straight at him, and smirked, "I'd rather you pull the wig off."

"*Bet-sy*," he countered authoritatively, peering over his glasses.

"Okay, you win. I'll keep my options open."

It was already late afternoon by the time we headed home. The support group was meeting that night, and I had planned to go. I hadn't missed a meeting since I'd first attended, but I didn't want to leave Alex. I knew I had upset him that afternoon, and I thought that if I cooked dinner and talked about work, he would believe I'd just had a little outburst and had gotten over it. He didn't believe it. He would tell me later that he was just as scared as I was. Scared of that new door that had opened. Scared that I wouldn't pass through it, even if it became my only option. And scared that neither of us was up to that challenge. It would require enormous energy to push thoughts of a transplant aside while we focused on the Zevalin treatment.

But obtaining this new drug would not be easy. Zevalin is not stocked on the shelves of drugstores, but made to order and sent to the facility where it is administered. And although it had been approved by the FDA, insurance companies had not yet approved payment for it, and it would take herculean efforts to persuade our insurance carrier to cover it. I knew none of this at the time, but the facts began to unfold over the next several days as it became clear that, among other things, Dr. Kaminski had to write a letter of medical need. In other words, some bean counter was about to decide whether my life was worth saving.

Carolyn protected me from the details of this as much as possible, reminding me that I had enough stress without this additional worry. She promised to do what was necessary to make sure that insurance covered the treatment, and I believed her. No one at U of M had ever let me down yet. She'll never admit to the hours she spent wrangling with the insurance company, but she prevailed, and we will be forever grateful. We'd have been in big trouble otherwise.

By then, I was feeling the full blown effects of Decadron and was sleeping very little. And still manipulating my mind, chemo brain remembered the last thing it heard, which was that I had ten months to live — if, of course, I was lucky. Exhausted and plagued by relapse, I could barely think. I neither laughed nor cried. I simply existed, waiting and wondering if Zevalin would work — and for how long.

I no longer hoped to see my grandchildren graduate from college. Seeing them start kindergarten seemed a stretch. I'd wanted a new winter coat, but how many winters would I get out of it? I stopped thinking about a new coat. The newspaper subscription was due for renewal. I had a choice of paying for three months, six months or a year. I paid for three months and wondered if that was too long. And more pieces of my life fell victim to lymphoma when I resigned that week from every committee I sat on.

Early the following week, I had to see yet another stranger, the radiation oncologist who would actually pump me full of Zevalin.

Although he would be my personal cellular executioner, I dreaded going to another doctor. I shouldn't have. Dr. Jafar would have made a wonderful coach. He examined the playing field — me — and with the greatest of confidence, explained the defensive play — Zevalin. And then he wheeled around on his stool, took a deep breath, placed both hands on his knees and began to deliver the best pep talk I've ever had.

"Look," he said. "Until they've been around for awhile, there is a lot we don't know about new drugs. But what we do know is that Zevalin can work for you." Little could he have known that I was sitting on the table thinking, "Yeah, for ten months."

Dr. Jafar continued, and passionately. "You know, Betsy," yes, he actually used my name, "I've been a physician for a long time. I've seen people live who shouldn't have, medically speaking. I've seen people die who, medically, should have lived. Sometimes there is no reason for either outcome. What I've observed over the years is that the people who fight back, whose will to live is the strongest, who maintain positive outlooks, they're most often the ones who beat the odds. I will give you the best medicine that is currently available, but you have a job to do, too. You go home and eat right. Get plenty of rest. Love your family. Laugh often. And don't give up — not for a minute."

I sat on the table listening to this speech, speechless. There was a doctor telling me I had a chance! My eyes grew a little misty and my spirit soared. Maybe I could make it for eleven months, even twelve? Did I dare hope for longer? I would gladly follow Dr. Jafar's instructions if that meant boosting my chance for success, but did ten minutes of sleep a week qualify as plenty of rest? Decadron wasn't allowing much more.

My outlook began to lift as Labor Day weekend and the arrival of Juli and the babies approached. A full eight months had passed since I had seen them, and just imagining holding those babies put a smile on my face. I didn't want to miss one waking moment of their visit, but I was somewhat concerned that I would not be able to match their energy levels. Two days before their arrival, I was happily buying bubbles and baby food and never gave a second thought to the blood test I had that morning.

On Thursday, exactly one hour before leaving to meet Juli, Skye and Nicholas at the airport, I was jittering with euphoric anticipation when the phone rang. It was the doctor at the new clinic. The blood test from two days earlier indicated that my lymphocyte count had soared to twenty, twice the high end of the range in which Zevalin could safely be administered. Although the test dose was scheduled for the following Wednesday, it was doubtful, he said, that I was a candidate for Zevalin. He asked me to have a blood test the following Tuesday, and then he couldn't get off the phone fast enough.

I wanted to clinch my fists and scream. I wanted to throw things. I wanted to hit something. I wanted to scream louder and harder. But as usual, I turned to Alex, who thankfully happened to be home working, and sobbed uncontrollably on his shoulder. My body tensed, and I think it would have collapsed into a heap on the floor had Alex not supported it in his arms. A second relapse and now this? Oh, dear God. What did it mean if I couldn't take Zevalin? What would stop this monster that seemed so determined to murder me? Was there any bottom to this emotional abyss?

I dragged myself upstairs to wash my face and to change the shirt onto which mascara-stained tears had fallen. I left Alex downstairs, standing in the kitchen, arms by his side. His shoulders drooped, his eyebrows were drawn together, his color drained. He looked so weary. When I returned downstairs, he hadn't moved. He wanted to drive me to the airport, but luggage and carseats left little room for another passenger. I promised him I was okay, at least to drive, and we melted together in a long embrace. As I opened the door to the garage, I turned my head over my shoulder and said, "You might want to change your shirt. My mascara's not your color." He didn't even smile.

● ● ●

Miracles happen everyday. Change your perception of what a miracle is and you'll see them all around you.
— Jon Bon Jovi

15. | THE POWER OF LOVE

O n the way to the airport, my mind was reeling so fast that my head felt like it would explode. Why, I wondered, was my body so intent on killing me? And why had Dr. Doom delivered such horrific news without suggesting an alternate plan or at least giving me some reassurance? Didn't he have a clue that news like that would devastate anybody? Did I have any options? Was I facing a transplant in thirty days? Sixty? What if Karen didn't match? Would anyone? What if no one did? How many months — or was it weeks — did I have to live?

And just why had Dr. Doom waited two whole days to call me? The results of blood tests can be reported in minutes, not days. It was my blood and I had a right to know quickly when it misbehaved. Yeah, I wanted to shoot the messenger. His delivery was terrible. His timing was worse. Had he called even an hour earlier, we might have had time to find out if other options were available prior to the dreaded bone marrow transplant — if a suitable donor could even be found in a short time. But there was no time for that now. Juli and her babies were somewhere over Ohio and approaching Detroit fast.

Fighting back tears, I desperately wanted to call somebody to help me cope with this maelstrom. Dr. Kaminski and Judy were on vacation. I thought of calling Carolyn, but I was well aware that I would have started bawling again if I even heard her voice, and my puffy eyes and red nose from the last cry needed the drive time to recover before I met Juli. Alex was too numb to think of calling Carolyn for me, and I was too numb to think of asking him. Somehow I had to pull myself together, to draw on my own reserves. I hoped I had some left.

I pulled into the parking garage, wiped my eyes dry, and hoped they would stay that way. Waiting for Juli, Nicholas and Skye at the baggage claim area, I wondered how the kids would react to me. Nicholas, at 18 months, hadn't even been walking when I saw him last. He wouldn't possibly remember me. I knew that Skye, who had just turned three, would.

My heart raced with excitement when I saw them in the distance. Spotting me, Skye pulled away from Juli and ran with outstretched arms, knocking me off my knees as I knelt to catch her. At last her little arms were around my neck and I smothered her with kisses. "Grammy, Grammy, I love you," she said. Her exuberance immediately banished my anguish to the farthest recesses of my mind. And at last I embraced Juli, the daughter I had missed so terribly all year. Nicholas, though smiling, wasn't sure who I was. We would have to get to know each other again.

Surrounded by the three people I had missed the most, we headed home to play for the next four days, and I resolved to make every minute count. Throwing caution to the wind, I ventured out into the germ-infested world, determined to enjoy Juli and my grandchildren. Did anybody know when — or if — I could do it again? We played on swings and slides in parks. We toured the fire station and a hands-on museum for children. We spent a day at the Toledo Zoo. Even Juli cautioned me to remain outside the petting area, but I wasn't about to miss Skye's and Nicholas' giggles and squeals as they played with the baby animals. What difference would it make if I was going to die anyway?

Late Saturday afternoon, we visited a tiger exhibit and held baby tigers, much to the kids' delight. While there, Carolyn phoned to ask how I was feeling. "Fine," I assured her, without telling her what we were doing. I added, "Carolyn, it's Saturday afternoon. You must have better things to do than to call me. Go enjoy the rest of the weekend." In fact, Carolyn was not calling solely to inquire about how I felt. The real purpose of her call was to report that Karen's blood was incompatible with mine and to recommend that Juli's be typed. This was not good news, and subconsciously, I knew that my disease needed treatment far sooner than a donor could be found, but at the moment, I was too busy with my grandbabies and the tigers to care.

At home, we filled the jacuzzi with bubbles and became bubble monsters, amidst uproarious laughter. We chased each other around the house playing hide and seek. Skye and I baked cakes and cookies. And at night, we crawled up on the bed and read stories.

Afraid that my mangy head might frighten the kids, I always wore a knit cap when I wasn't wearing the wig. One evening, before I could stop him, Nicholas pulled off the cap, and both he and Skye immediately froze, staring at my head. Finally Skye asked, "Grammy, what happened to your hair?"

"I took some medicine that made it fall out," I answered.

"Oh, I not take that kind of medicine," she said, quickly resuming her laughter and nonstop chatter. Nicholas stroked my head as if it belonged to one of the baby goats at the zoo. And that was the end of that. Shouldn't I have known that kids accept far more than we adults realize?

For four days, uncertainty stayed in the background while laughter and play and hugs and kisses took center stage. Every moment with Juli and Skye and Nicholas gave me a precious memory and plenty of reminders of why I should fight for life with every ounce of my strength. And despite the potential crisis that lay ahead, my energy level rose to its highest level of the year.

Alex, on the other hand, was clearly distraught. He was pleasant enough but could scarcely manage a smile. His voice sounded flat and barely audible. His lifeless eyes seemed focused on something in the distance. His frequent hugs that weekend were powerful and poignant. Did I sense grief?

But we were both happy that Juli and the babies had come. They lifted me from an emotional abyss into which I immediately fell when they left. After dropping them off at the airport, I sobbed all the way back to Ann Arbor and the hospital for another blood test, wondering what my lymphocytes had been doing all weekend while the rest of me played. Had those murderous little cells been multiplying wantonly? I felt like a wounded, hunted animal.

My cell phone rang two hours after the blood test. Caller ID, indicating Dr. Doom, turned my stomach queasy. I barely managed to answer before voice mail picked up. "Hello," I said, trying to sound perfectly normal.

"Hello, Mrs. de Parry. I don't know how this happened, but your lymphocyte count dropped to two. Come on in tomorrow for the Zevalin." Astonished that my diabolical lymphocytes had changed their minds and given me a reprieve, I'm sure that my voice quivered as I thanked Dr. Doom for calling.

Jumping up and down with tears of joy falling down my cheeks, I excitedly dialed Alex's phone. "It's a miracle. My lymphocytes are down to two!" And then I became Ethel Merman, bellowing out in song, "I got Zevalin. I got Zevalin. I got Zevalin. Who could ask for anything more?" Never mind that I have a range of one note, which is reliably flat, the song said it all. Delivered from whatever disaster might have awaited us had my lymphocyte count remained high, we were more excited than two kids on Christmas morning. And that night, we both badly sang Ethel's song with our own words as we danced around the kitchen. Okay, I danced around the kitchen. Alex is much too reserved for such silliness, but his broad smile was a perfectly suitable dance partner.

Skeptics may attribute the fall in my lymphocyte count to Decadron, but they'd certainly disregarded the drug the previous week. I believe the fall was the direct result of hundreds of baby kisses and all the love and happiness I experienced that weekend. Scientists can't explain it, but they do know that endorphins — those chemicals which control the body's reaction to pain and stress — can have a mighty impact on our immune systems, and I believe that my endorphins gobbled up those unruly lymphocytes, thanks to Juli and Nicholas and Skye and the power of love.

Whatever the reason, Alex and I were, of course, relieved, and yes, I was dancing in the kitchen, but months of challenges had worn us down. And the wild swing of emotions during the previous three weeks had left us with barely enough energy to hope that RIT would rescue me from the jaws of death.

● ● ●

16. | CANCER MEETS ITS MATCH

On September 4, Alex chauffeured me and my low lymphocyte count to the other hospital. We weren't sure what to expect. As approved by the FDA, RIT is given in two doses a week apart. The first dose consists of a monoclonal antibody — Rituxan, in the case of Zevalin — followed by a small, test dose of a radiolabeled antibody, which is an antibody to which a small radioactive molecule is attached. The purpose of the test dose in Zevalin is to make sure that the radiolabeled antibody is properly distributed in the body. And surely, the radioactive component meant Hazmat suits and lead-lined rooms, which is where I fully expected to go after the Rituxan infusion.

It turns out that I had to leave the comfort of my infusion room because there was a backlog of patients and the room was needed for someone else. Alex and I were escorted not to a lead-lined room but to a supply closet where half the cabinet doors were flung open, exposing all sorts of medical supplies. It was a mess. Perplexed, we were told to wait there. Within minutes, a kid in jeans and sneakers arrived with the test dose. Come on, I was to be shot up with radiation. Where was the fanfare?

There in the disarray of that room, I sat in the only chair. Alex held my hand. And ten minutes later, radioactive isotopes swam in my veins, thanks to a kid who had just graduated from high school. Alex and I laughed all the way home.

Two days later, we celebrated our anniversary. Alex had asked what I wanted and I had jokingly said, "Your karma. Or how about some new blood?" We made dinner at home and were happy to celebrate the day.

He'd also asked if there was anything I would like to do. "Go to Hell," I deadpanned. His eyes widened questioningly. "I want to go to Hell." And so we did. Hell, Michigan is a village northwest of Ann Arbor. Mimicking the "Got Milk?" ad campaign, I made a "Got Lymphoma?" banner. In Hell, I placed it so that the entire sign read "Got Lymphoma? Welcome to Hell." Alex took pictures of me by the sign, and I emailed them to several friends who saw the humor in it far more than he did.

On Wednesday, September 11, the sun was just beginning to peer over the horizon when we left home and headed to the hospital for the full blast of Zevalin, which consists of Rituxan plus the full dose of radioactive isotopes. Alex and I spoke of the date and grieved for the thousands of families whose loved ones had lost their lives one year earlier. I suspected that any one of them would have traded places with me that day for an extra year of life, even if it meant having lymphoma.

It seemed irreverent to hope for a personal victory on a day of national mourning, and yet we did hope that the day would spring new life into me. Halfway to the hospital, the sun's rays were bathing the earth with radiant beams, and I broke into song, "Oh what a beautiful morning. Oh what a beautiful day. I've got a beautiful feeling. Everything's going our way." Alex smiled and patted my hand and failed to mention that my vocal chords needed tuning.

Shortly before the infusion, we met with Dr. Doom who, again, reminded us that there was no way of knowing how long Zevalin would work — six months maybe, he predicted. Wait a minute. He had said ten months at our earlier meeting. Why was he stealing four months from me? Did I look like I had an expiration date stamped on my forehead? Annoyed, I told him to quit worrying, that I would be around to change Alex's bedpan in our old age. I figured that was a little more courteous than telling him to shut the hell up.

I was so exuberant that nothing could dampen my mood. Almost nothing. Moments before the Rituxan infusion began, a sharp pain suddenly stabbed at my right side. I joked to Alex, "Maybe I got too excited this morning. I think I'm having an anxiety attack." Except that it wasn't funny. I could barely breathe. The nurse checked with the doctor who ordered Motrin, and the infusion, preceded by Benadryl, got underway.

This was the Big Moment. The End of Treatment. The day we would exit Cancer Land. I was sure of it. For Alex, I'd brought pom-poms and a card which thanked him for being my biggest cheerleader, and he laughed when I gave them to him. Mr. Reserved even waved the pom-poms and chanted, as Benadryl sent me to sleep, "Kill the cells. Kill the cells. Go Zevalin."

Four hours later, the Rituxan infusion was complete and I awoke, still in pain and breathing as shallowly as possible. Again the nurse checked with Dr. Doom who didn't bother to walk across the hall to see me, but instead sent the nurse back with additional Motrin and a bomb for an explanation. She reported matter-of-factly, "The doctor feels that the cancer has spread to your bone. Here's a prescription for pain." And then she left the room. Stunned, I looked at Alex and said, "Great, now we deal with bone cancer. That's nice and fatal."

Still groggy, I didn't fully absorb the explanation. Alex, of course, was completely alert, and weeks later would tell me that he was furious that Dr. Doom had sent a nurse to deliver such unhappy news — and on what basis? No X-ray, no CT scan, no other test had been taken on which to base that assumption. No doctor had examined me for this symptom. And no one made a single suggestion about what we should do if it were true, unless you count the prescription for painkillers. And if that was the best they could do for me, the outlook was indeed bleak. Just as the one treatment that might save my life was about to enter my body, Dr. Doom stole Alex's hope, and he immediately began to ponder how abruptly and drastically things can change and to wonder what horrors would be next.

Alex would also tell me later that I seemed to have forgotten the news quickly and was excitedly declaring, "By this time tomorrow, I'll be cancer-free." Thank goodness for Benadryl. Meanwhile, panicked and angry, he was struggling to appear calm. He wanted to leave the room to call Judy or Dr. Kaminski, thinking that they had never, not once, drawn conclusions without having results of appropriate tests on which to base conclusions, nor had they ever left us dangling with bad news without offering some reassurance to offset it. But Zevalin was on its way, and he remained by my side.

I got to stay in my tiny room for this dose, and we were joined by several doctors in their white coats — no Hazmat suits — who wanted to learn how to administer RIT. Except for Alex, the mood was festive, as if some spectacular show were about to take place. The star soon arrived neatly packed in a metal box, and Dr. Jafar inserted a special tube in my arm through which it would flow.

As the drug dripped into my veins, tears of joy spilled down my cheeks. Alex and I knew that RIT was the very best chance we had to reclaim our lives, and he nodded in agreement when I spoke of my gratitude to the countless people who had propelled us to that moment in time: patients who had participated in clinical trials, companies and non-profits and individuals who had supported the science, and of course, the scientists themselves. And then I whispered to Alex so that no one would hear, "Thank God, especially, for Dr. Kaminski. This may not be his drug, but it's his theory."

Squeezing my hand, Alex tried to smile, but he looked so anxious. I would later learn that the tears that welled in his eyes were not tears of joy, but tears of impending grief. Dr. Doom had sent him into emotional freefall.

Within a half hour, my cells were thoroughly bathed in radioactive missiles. As we exited the hospital, I was sure they were busy detonating every malignant cell in my body. Pain and all, I threw my hands in the air, danced in circles, and reveled, "Yea, I'm done. I'm down to one blood test a week. We have our life back." Why did the look on Alex's face seem to disagree with me? Because he knew better. He was simply too kind to remind me that my body was so toxified from months of chemical warfare that it would need some time to recover. And there was that little bone cancer issue.

Radioactive missiles and all, I didn't glow in the dark that night, and I was far more alert the following day. The pain was severe and breathing was difficult, but I didn't fill the prescription for pain. I remembered its cause was supposed to be bone cancer, but I didn't reach for my safety net — Dr. Kaminski and Judy — nor would I let Alex. I begged him to give me one day — just one day — to believe that I was cancer-free before I faced any subsequent setbacks. And all day I hoped that the pain would magically disappear. It didn't.

With all the setbacks I'd had, I felt like a hypochondriac by the time I called Judy the following morning. Not surprisingly, the pain earned me an immediate return visit to the clinic.

In the form of scans and ultrasounds, Dr. Kaminski ordered so many photographs of my interior that I joked that U of M would run out of film. By 6:00 p.m., he suspected that a small blood clot was the possible culprit, a far superior explanation than bone cancer, I thought. He couldn't be certain without an angiogram, which, since it was Friday, could not be done until the following Monday unless he admitted me to the hospital. Another stay in Hotel Hell? I don't think so. Ever cautious, I knew that Dr. Kaminski would not let me return home if he believed I was in any danger. To be safe, he prescribed a blood thinner that I was to take over the weekend.

There was just one small problem. The blood thinner required self-injections — twice daily. I could find friends to administer shots once a day, but twice? Dr. Kaminski hadn't heard about Alex's and my cowardice before, and he chuckled when I told him that Alex had once planned to become a surgeon. "Probably a good thing he chose another line of work," he said. Judy gave me the first shot that afternoon, and once again stayed well past clinic hours to assist with my care.

Alex and I were so relieved. Almost anything was better than bone cancer. But whom could I call on to give me shots twice a day? After dinner, Alex rose from the table, walked to the bar and poured himself a glass of wine. And then he turned to me, grinned broadly, raised his glass and said, "Here's to your new nurse. I'll give you the shots."

"Sure you will," I laughed. "You almost passed out when Sandy tried to hand you the syringe."

"I can do it," he tried to assure me. "I just need to psych myself up for it. I don't want to hurt you."

"Here's your big chance," I teased.

How was Alex not going to hurt me, considering the fact that he had never held a syringe, much less emptied its contents into another human being? We got an orange and one of the used syringes from the Neupogen, and he practiced injecting the fruit over and over again.

By morning, when it was time for the next shot, I was certain that we'd be found passed out on the floor with a syringe dangling from my leg if we foolishly proceeded. Alex, on the other hand, was intent on accomplishing the mission. Nervous but determined, he practiced a few more times on the orange while I panicked and paced around the kitchen island muttering absurdities. "Oh God, it's Dr. Mengele reincarnated and experimenting again. Alex, no matter how badly you hurt me, I swear I'll still love you. Don't you want to re-think this? If you don't give me the shots and it is a blood clot, maybe it will hit my heart and we'll both be out of our misery."

"Will you just be quiet? I'm ready," he said, holding the syringe straight in the air. It looked like a rifle, and I waited for someone to

announce, "Ready. Aim. Fire." And then I'd be gone — after an agonizing bombardment, of course.

"Okay, let's get this over with." I whimpered.

I sat down, swabbed my leg with alcohol and pinched my thigh
for him. And then I closed my eyes and waited for unskilled hands
to inflict grisly torture. The waiting was interminable. What was he
doing? I moaned and moaned and moaned and finally begged
through gritted teeth, "Alex, just push it in. I swear I won't scream
no matter how much it hurts. Just get it over with."

"Open your eyes," Alex replied.

"I can't until you're done," I groaned.

"Betsy, just open them up." Grimacing, I opened one eye, and
much to my surprise, the empty syringe was in front of my face. "I'm
done. It's over," he grinned. My eyes wide with wonder, I threw my
arms around his neck and we laughed and laughed. Alex was pretty
proud of his new skill, and I was proud of him. It was one of many
skills that cancer had compelled us to learn, but we'd paid an exor-
bitant emotional price for our education. Keeping that thought to
myself, I simply teased Alex that he should re-think medical school,
and he smiled.

On Monday, I was to have the angiogram, a procedure which
detects blockages by moving a catheter through the blood vessels.
The catheter is normally inserted through a small incision in the
groin area, but because I had been on blood thinners and had taken
Zevalin five days earlier, Dr. Kaminski ordered the catheter to enter
through an IV in my arm. Sandy, his nurse, inserted the IV and
attached a tube through which the catheter could wind through my
body.

On the way to the radiology department, I fully expected that I
would get three or four brains for the price of one. What I didn't
expect was entertainment to be thrown in for free. Once I had
stretched out on the table in the dimly lighted room, two people
entered through the rear door. I recognized one as a nurse, but the
other wore apparel I had never seen before. The young man's head

was covered with an oversized baby blue hat with an elastic band around its perimeter. The hat complimented his baby blue vest and matching knee-length skirt, both fashioned of what I presumed to be trendy hospital fabric — lead. The skirt exposed several inches of hairy legs that extended to black socks and shoes. Thinking that this young man's coordinated outfit was at least somewhat more fashionable than the hospital gown I wore, I considered asking him if he would like to swap, but he had already introduced himself and begun to explain the procedure. And then he noticed the tube dangling from the IV in my arm.

"Oh," he exclaimed excitedly. "I've never done this through the arm." Turning to the nurse, he asked, "What size line do we use for this?" She didn't know.

He told me to stay put and that he would be right back. Like I was going somewhere, I thought. Within moments, he returned with another young man who wore an identical outfit but who knew no more about the size line than he did. Both were very excited about learning a new way to perform the procedure, though. Again the first young man told me to stay put and that he would return shortly, and again he returned with another young man who wore the same ensemble.

The blue-skirted, hairy-legged trio huddled together, studying the tube affixed to my arm with great fascination, and it was all I could do to refrain from bursting out laughing. I knew very well that these young men were residents and that their attending physician would soon join us, but I offered to help anyway. "Hey, if you guys can round up a manual, I'll read it to you while you work."

All three lifted their heads and stared at me as blankly as Alex does when I wisecrack — which amused me even more. And then one of them said, as if I were serious, "We don't have a manual. We have Dr. Cho." That was it for me. I burst out laughing just as Dr. Cho arrived wearing a blue vest and a skirt that hung to his ankles. I almost asked if radiology residents get long skirts instead of diplomas for graduation, but I kept that one to myself.

The hardest part of the whole procedure was trying to stay still when I wanted to shake with laughter — which, of course, is not the best thing to do when a catheter is winding through your heart. When it was all over, The Blue Skirts had found nothing unusual and the blood thinners were history.

Alex pretended to pout when I told him he'd have to close his medical practice. No more shots. No more tests. And no definitive reason for the pain. Using its astonishing array of tools, medical science had determined, through the process of elimination, that I had no bone cancer, no blood clots, and no interior disorder other than the one we already knew about. That was great news. As it turned out, the pain took four weeks to subside on its own, and its cause was never found. Our mysterious bodies sometimes outwit the best doctors — even the ones who actually try to find causes for symptoms.

At last, I presumed, life would return to normal. I might as well have presumed that palm trees grow in the Arctic. It would take some time for both my body and our emotions to heal.

A week after Zevalin, I stopped taking Industrial Strength No-Doz — Decadron — cold turkey. For the six weeks that I'd consumed it, I'd averaged a couple of hours of sleep a night. It's no wonder that I turned into Rip Van Winkle after stopping the medication. Two days later, I slept for thirty-six hours straight, so soundly that Alex worried if I would ever wake up.

For the next five weeks, I slept nine to ten hours each night in addition to napping once or twice a day. Between sleep, overwhelming fatigue thwarted my attempts to resurface into the life I had once known. I didn't dare make the forty-five minute drive, one way, into our Detroit area suppliers. I didn't dare commit to a meeting that wasn't absolutely necessary. My expectations of returning to our normal life far exceeded reality. My body required time to heal from the cumulative effect of several months of toxic drugs followed so closely by RIT.

Days seemed like weeks as Alex and I waited, wondered and worried if the cancer had finally succumbed. Ever so cautiously, we dared to hope that it had and carefully guarded our fragile hope from anything or anyone who might dampen it.

Protocol dictated that I return to the other clinic for followup tests, including weekly blood draws. During all the months that blood was drawn at U of M, Judy had always let me know its status by phone or by email within a matter of hours, another gesture that said, "We're watching out for you. You have enough to worry about without waiting and worrying about test results." At the other clinic, no one ever called. No doubt Judy had spoiled me, but I was at least confident that someone was looking at the results of tests. At the other clinic, I had to wait days and then beg someone to copy the reports. Not only did I wonder what my blood was doing, but I also wondered if anyone ever looked at the reports. Hence I always sent them to Judy. At least I knew she'd look out for me. And she did. My counts were behaving properly, but we'd have to wait for a followup up exam and CT scan to know whether Zevalin was working.

And protocol dictated that I see Dr. Doom for the followup exam six weeks after treatment. Protocol be damned. I wasn't about to return to the doctor who had stamped an expiration date on me and terrorized us with baseless conclusions. I was soon back under Dr. Kaminski's care.

During the fourth week after treatment, Alex came home from work and went straight to the sink to wash his hands, just as he does every day. He stopped suddenly, thrust his wet hands into his pockets, pulled them out disbelievingly, and thrust them in again. "What are you doing?" I asked.

His color faded and his words could scarcely form. "I just realized my wedding ring is gone. I had it this morning," he mumbled, staring at his empty ring finger.

I put my arms around him and whispered, "Oh Alex, it's only a ring. We'll either find it or replace it. Don't worry." He did worry. That ring was the tangible, permanent possession that would outlast me.

We searched his truck, and for days, he retraced his steps and searched jobsites with his metal detector, but the ring was gone. It couldn't possibly have fallen from his finger. For months I had watched him fidget with it, twisting it around and around and then pulling it slightly over his knuckle and pushing it back again. Somewhere we suspected he had pulled it over his knuckle once too often. He couldn't have felt much worse.

During the fifth and sixth weeks after Zevalin, I regained some of my energy and slept less during the day. My hair began to sprout and I giggled when I brought my razor out of retirement, changed the blade and shaved my legs for the first time in months. My brain began to return from vacation, and I could remember what day it was and recite paragraphs in our building contract. Alex and I were pleased, and our optimism grew stronger each day.

There was, however, one small dilemma. I'd lost interest in everything about my job. The process of building homes was no longer exciting. Homes themselves became shelters from the elements. Nothing more. Nothing less. Choosing sinks and windows and carpet and tile seemed utterly insignificant. If a tub held water, what more could anyone want? No sense agonizing over the make and model. Intellectually, I knew how exciting building a new home can and should be, and I had always been passionate about helping our clients through every phase, but cancer had replaced my passion with apathy. How would I regain my interest? Or would I?

Six weeks after treatment, I walked into U of M for a CT scan, wondering if all the effort had been worth it. What would the pictures reveal? Dr. Kaminski called to report the news, his voice resounding with pleasure as he told me that all lymph nodes were within normal range. I grinned from ear to ear. I'm pretty sure he did, too. Six weeks wasn't a long time, much too early to consider using the word "remission," but Dr. Kaminski and I agreed that for now, I was on vacation from cancer. And that was good enough for me.

● ● ●

Oh, my friend, it's not what they take away from you that counts.
It's what you do with what you have left.
— *Hubert Humphrey*

17. | NEXT STOP: LIMBO LAND

At last I realized what Dr. Kaminski's words had really meant during our first meeting all those months ago. Figuratively, he had said, "Cancer is a winding, obstacle-laden road, but we are here to guide you. Here, take our hands. We will firmly hold yours and lead you, as best we can, to recovery." I had taken the many hands that had reached out to me and gratefully held on for dear life.

Now we had arrived at our destination and it was time to let go. But how? I was now traveling the road alone, without tests or appointments for another six whole weeks, during which any hint of pain, any twitch sent me into tizzy of fear. The same girl who had once ignored every little ache and pain now overreacted to each and every one. If I broke a fingernail, lymphoma was surely back. Okay, I wasn't that neurotic, but I came close. I still feared that going into crowds could expose me to germs and send me straight back to Hotel Hell. And the absence of weekly blood draws meant that I had no idea if my own blood was scheming against me. If my medical team was no longer watching out for me, who was? As long as I was being tested and treated, people were working hard to save my life, and I was safe from harm. Now what?

I'd spent endless hours fantasizing about how life would be after treatment ended, and I was ecstatic that it had, but what was I supposed to do? What purpose did I have? I had traveled so far from the healthy world that I didn't know how to get back. I was living in limbo, somewhere between the recent struggle to survive and uncomfortable future uncertainties.

Physically, I began to recover. About six weeks after treatment, I stayed awake all day, which is hardly a spectacular achievement under ordinary circumstances. But cancer is not an ordinary circumstance, and that first day of wakefulness was a joyful signal that recovery was possible.

Somewhere in the distance, I glimpsed my old busy life looming, yet it eluded me as I stumbled toward it. My *self* had to learn to live in the same body that had just tried to kill me. How could I trust it not to pull that same stunt again?

And just where was my old self — the self that had once consisted of many pieces scattered far and wide to make me whole? When cancer had called, I had quickly gathered all my pieces to focus on reaching a single goal, a goal I hoped I'd reached. Suddenly, all the things that I had ignored during my illness were back and important again, but how would I disassemble my "single purpose" self and return to the multiple roles I had once played?

And just what was I supposed to talk about at a social or business function? The latest cancer article I'd read? Hawkeye's escapades? How excited I was to be able to stay awake all day? No one wanted to hear that, but I had nothing else to say to friends and colleagues. Stepping back among them was painfully lonely because I was no longer like them. I felt like a stranger in a world that was familiar but in which I no longer fit.

Treatment was over — for now — but it seemed that cancer had won after all. It had usurped my momentum, stolen my passion and left me in an emotional vacuum from which I knew not how to escape. How ironic, I thought, that miraculous drugs could rid my body of something so invasive as cancer and still leave me feeling so

vulnerable. So timid. So empty. I guessed the doctors had no anti-
dote for that. I'd have to find it myself. But where? And how?

Somehow I had to put all this into perspective. I told myself that
I was still the same person — not just a person who had once had
cancer. I reminded myself that I was the sum of all my parts and that
cancer had only been a small fraction of my life. And yet, it left more
scars and doubts than any experience that preceded it. A previous
divorce or cold don't predict a future divorce or cold. Cancer pre-
dicts a future that holds frequent tests and potentially unimaginable
medical procedures. How was I to learn to live with uncertainty as
my constant companion?

And had cancer really been a "journey" as it is often described?
From the beginning, "journey" had never sounded like an accurate
description, and I'd often thought, "If cancer is a journey, I want a
new travel agent." Cancer Land was a destination to which I had
never wanted to journey in the first place. I preferred to think of life
as a journey. Cancer was just a bad detour to an awful place that had
robbed me of my physical well-being, my freedom, my confidence,
my dreams and my ability to protect the people I love the most from
fear and worry. I don't recommend booking a reservation, but somehow I'd have to face the distinct possibility that my body would
book another one for me.

And how could I possibly re-establish myself as dependable? I
knew how much Alex had shouldered during my illness, and I genuinely wanted to remove the extra load from him, but I couldn't
muster any interest in work. Ever so gently, he tried to coax me back
by including me in meetings and asking my opinion about a variety
of things. I participated, but only half-heartedly and only because I
felt badly that he had carried my share of the load for so many
months. He was incredibly patient. Had I been in his shoes, I might
have screamed at me, "Listen, lady, you've been sick. It's over. Get a
grip." I repeated those words to myself over and over again, but it
didn't help.

By mid-November, I consciously set myself up to take small steps toward normalcy. I forced myself to accomplish something every day at work. I dared to go to lunch with a friend and silently cheered when I only thought — not panicked — about germs lurking in the restaurant's kitchen. Alex and I invited friends for dinner and delighted that cancer was a mere footnote to the conversation.

I ventured back onto our jobsites more regularly and ran into subcontractors I hadn't seen in months. Each and every one told the same story. They were happy to see me alive and well. Alex had looked exhausted and hadn't been himself for months. Sometimes he'd told them to do one thing when something else was needed. As one of them told me, "We just ignored the old boy and did what we knew he meant."

Alex and I put our house back on the market, and I was proud that I could manage to keep it in showing condition every day. I still dreaded dismantling one house and setting up another, but considering everything else we had gone through, moving was a minor inconvenience. We sold it in five weeks.

On Thanksgiving we had eleven people for dinner. I thoroughly enjoyed cooking far more food than we could eat and engaging in lively conversation with family and friends. More than any year before, we had so very much for which to be thankful.

By then, a whole month had passed without my calling Judy for a single ailment, but most days I could scarcely resist the urge to call and ask, "Are you sure I'm okay? May I please have a blood test just to make sure?" And yes, this is the same girl who hated needles just a few months earlier. I still hate them, but those internal audits had kept us all informed about what my blood was doing, and I wondered what shenanigans it might pull if we weren't watching.

In early December, I was immensely relieved to have blood drawn, another CT scan, and to see Dr. Kaminski and Judy again. In the reception area, I commented to Alex how our perception of waiting for them had changed during the year. At first exasperated by any appointment that pulled us from our own schedules, we had quickly learned that if they were running late, it simply meant that they were taking time to help individual patients with their own special needs and that they would do the same for me when our turn came. I was quite grateful that they didn't practice assembly line medicine.

Dr. Kaminski and Judy gave me a thorough inspection and reported that the pictures looked great. Wow — three months had passed and no sign of cancer! Dr. Kaminski and Judy beamed. I beamed with them and thought how nice it was for them to see the fruits of their labor and to deliver good news for a change. I also teased Alex that we should put those CT scan pictures on our Christmas cards.

I asked Dr. Kaminski how long we could expect Zevalin to last and what options we would have if it stopped working. Of course there's no way to predict how long any treatment will last, but based on experience with his Bexxar patients whose disease was as chemo-resistant as mine was, Dr. Kaminski told us that we could reasonably hope for a couple of years. He added that the time frame could move farther out, depending on the depth of remission over the next several months. And if the disease returned, we may or may not have other options before proceeding to a bone marrow transplant. I was still determined to defy the odds and the medians, but recurrence hung over my head like the sword of Damocles.

Alex and I met with Dr. Voravit Ratanatharathorn of the Blood and Marrow Transplant Unit on December 3. Emotionally, that meeting was both a setback and an awakening. As I had read, the procedure is risky and unpleasant, and it requires a lengthy stay in Hotel Hell and an even more lengthy recovery period at home. And I'd probably be a goner if it failed. Dr. Ratanatharathorn and Dr. Kaminski decided that I would proceed to transplant only if necessary, but I was scared to death that I may someday have to face that option. And just then, I wasn't ready for another fight. I was still licking my wounds from the last one.

Until our consultation, I hadn't realized that U of M was searching so hard for a donor, but we learned that they had found one. Only one. Out of 8 million potential donors at that time. Transplant patients aren't allowed to know the identity of their donors until one year has passed after the transplant, but we did learn that mine was a 41-one-year-old man who lived in another country. He was told that my medical condition had improved and that his donation wasn't needed at the moment. I prayed that he would be available if it was.

Alex and I went out for dinner after our consultation. At the restaurant, tears spilled down my cheeks as I thought of this donor who was willing to give me a chance to live — a man I had never met and who would receive nothing for his donation. Can anyone be more unselfish?

The consultation also raised again all the uncertainty I would have to learn to face. Fear of becoming bedridden crept in. Of becoming dependent. And useless. And of dying. It was time to have another heart-to-heart with myself. I asked myself if my future — or anyone's — comes with a guarantee. No, it doesn't. If I worried about becoming bedridden or undergoing horrible future treatments, would worry change the outcome? No. Would worrying today about things I can't control tomorrow make me miserable? Yes. And if I were miserable, wouldn't everyone around me be miserable, too? Yes. Did I want that? No. Could I set goals and work each day to reach them? Yes. Could I focus on each day and do one, maybe two or three, things to make someone else happy? Yes.

Oh, I was being so strong and so reasonable, I told myself. Couldn't I ever allow myself to wallow in a little self-pity? Okay, self, you can have that luxury. Just don't let it last long.

I quickly concluded that fear of future uncertainties could easily rob me of present joys. When fears crept in, they launched action to push them aside. I got busy at work. Called a friend. Took a walk. Listened to whatever music made me happy at the time. Baked a cake and gave it away. Called Alex and told him I loved him. Looked at pictures of Skye and Nicholas. I did whatever it took to banish the uncertainties at any given moment, and sometimes the effort was far more difficult than it had been during treatment. But the price of giving up was far too high. After all, I'd gone through treatment to stay alive, and alive was what I wanted to be in every sense of the word.

During the second week in December, Alex called from one of our jobsites for clarification about a client's tile selection. Without hesitation, I told him to stay there and that I would meet him in five minutes. On the drive over, I realized that this was the old me! I hadn't just answered Alex's question on the phone. I'd jumped in my car to visually show him what would have been nearly impossible to explain on the phone. Sensing my old interest returning, we both smiled broadly when I arrived.

The following week Alex and I were studying plans for a spec home we would soon begin. He suggested eliminating a small second floor balcony with balustrades. Wide-eyed, I implored, "Alex, you *have* to build that balcony. Those balustrades make the whole front of the house. You *can't* eliminate them."

"Maybe I liked it better when you were asleep," he snickered, grinning from ear to ear. We both knew that my interest was another sign of recovery which we wouldn't have recognized as such if we hadn't been looking.

On December 17, an advisory panel to the FDA at last recommended approval for Bexxar, the first step toward final approval. Alex and I heard the news the following morning, and that night, Beethoven's Ninth Symphony, Ode to Joy, seemed an appropriate accompaniment to the toast we made to Dr. Kaminski's success.

Two days later we joyously flew to West Palm Beach for the first time in a year. By then I'd nearly completed this manuscript up to this point, but I'd wanted to include Alex's side of the story as well as mine. He was, after all, my "co-patient," but one who'd almost always responded, "Don't worry about me," or "We'll do what we have to do," or some other equally unrevealing comment when I'd asked how he felt during all those months.

Alex had promised that I could interview him in Florida so that I could sprinkle his comments throughout the manuscript. For a man who likes to remain private, strong, and always in control, and one who naturally looks forward and not backward, I had thought that it would be difficult for Alex to reflect on and admit the fear and anxiety that had often overwhelmed him, especially knowing that he would be revealing himself not only to me but also to family, friends and anyone who read the story. But in a giant leap, he finally broke his stoic just-the-facts-ma'am silence. He answered every question I asked and many that I didn't, hoping that his revelations would be helpful to someone who may wear his uncomfortable shoes someday. To me, there was no great revelation. I had suspected everything Alex told me and was proud that he articulated his feelings better than I ever suspected he would.

● ● ●

*Life is like riding a bicycle — in order to keep your balance,
you must keep moving.*
— *Albert Einstein*

18. | REFLECTIONS

Throughout the next several days, Alex and I strolled the beach and sat by the pool reflecting on the past year. As bad as it had been, we knew that we had been among the luckiest of the unlucky. In the emergency room, what if Dr. Ketcham had turned to the more "important" traumas of the evening and dismissed my fever as something that would resolve on its own? When it did several days later, I would not have gone to another doctor. How much more trouble would I have been in by the time another symptom appeared?

And what if we hadn't lived in Ann Arbor? Of course there would have been other hospitals, but how lucky we were to live so close to one of the best. And we'd learned that a teaching hospital is meteorically different than what we had imagined. Though the ranking and financial future of any teaching hospital depends on its research, everyone I met at U of M seemed to clearly understand that *people* were their most valuable resource, mice and monkeys notwithstanding. Everyone seemed infinitely conscious that they were, in fact, treating people. Not lymphoma. Not pneumonia. Not broken arms.

No, I was never treated as a statistic or as a contributor to research. No one ever let cancer define me as a human being. Had

Dr. Kaminski merely prescribed medications, my body would most likely have healed the same way, but my psyche would have come away far more injured. He and Judy and Carolyn included sensitivity, intuition, and nurturing as an important part of the whole treatment, a part that buffered the falls and lifted our hope when we could find none. And by sharing the suffering of another human being, no doubt surrendering their own comfort at times to do so, they helped me to live, not simply exist, through the illness, and they taught me that medicine, done right, is profoundly personal. Alex and I agreed that their healing power had transcended the science of medicine.

We also knew, of course, that physicians make difficult life-and-death decisions and therefore cannot allow emotions to immobilize them. Yet we marveled at the balance that Dr. Kaminski and his colleagues had struck between caring so profoundly and remaining so objective. How he and Judy and all the others faced the horrors of cancer day in and day out was beyond our comprehension. We were deeply grateful that they could.

And it seemed to us that treatment at the Lymphoma Clinic — both medical and psychological — was truly custom tailored to recognize and respect the unique traits of every patient. No one ever had a canned script. Some months into treatment, I realized that Dr. Kaminski and Judy had quickly sized up my personality at our first meeting and had tailored subsequent conversations accordingly. When I finally figured out what they were doing, I found it somewhat entertaining that some of the very "people skills" training that I'd taken over the years was being used on me, and it made an enormous difference in how I responded to them and to the illness. In my humble opinion, all health care professionals should sneak out of medical school for a good seminar on understanding personality differences and delivering good customer service.

Yes, we had been lucky in so many ways, Alex and I thought. We'd had excellent insurance, no small children to further complicate matters, the flexibility of self-employment, and supportive family and friends who helped us through the emotional upheavals and the day-to-day challenges. Most of all, we had each other. Still, cancer had invaded every aspect of our life, and it had exacted a huge toll. Financially, our business goals had fallen far short of what we had expected for the year, but the good news was, we still had a business. Emotionally, Alex and I had neither sunk so low as some nor coped as well as others. As best we could, we'd simply muddled our way through a range and depth of emotions we could never have imagined before cancer, and thankfully, our marriage had withstood the pressures.

Alex and I agreed that the difference between past emotions and disease-related ones was a matter of intensity. During my illness, I wasn't just tired — I was exhausted. Annual celebrations — birthdays and anniversaries — seemed cause for a national holiday. A routine cookout with family and friends turned into a veritable feast. And I joked, "Yeah, the fear of losing my life was a tad stronger than the fear of losing a sale."

Strolling the beach one day, I asked Alex if he still thought about cancer every day. "Yeah, I do," he sadly admitted. "I don't worry so much anymore, but..." his voice drifted off.

"But what?" I asked.

After a few silent moments, he finally confided, "Okay. I know this isn't over yet. Sure, a truce has been called, and I pray the truce will last a very long time. But I can't completely push the thoughts aside. I wish I could."

I squeezed Alex's hand and confided my same fears. "I wonder if cancer will always be lurking in the background. When someone strikes up a conversation with 'How are you?' I wonder if I will ever be able to answer, 'Fine, thanks,' without silently adding, 'Except for the fact that I have a chronic disease called lymphoma and I might get a fever again one day and then I'll have to hightail it back to the doctor and find out if I need a bone marrow transplant and then I might die.'" Alex squeezed my hand back.

Beside the pool one afternoon, I said to Alex, "You know, we've never resolved what will happen if I get sick again. We really do need a backup plan." Alex reminded me that he had only agreed to divulge his feelings about the previous twelve months. I pushed, "So what will happen if I land in the hospital one day?"

"I'll deal with it if I have to," he said firmly.

"Alex, you buy car insurance. It doesn't mean you'll ever need it, but you wouldn't drive without it. Making a plan is the same thing," I pressed harder.

Alex sat up slightly in the lounge chair, looked over the top of his sunglasses, smiled broadly, and refused to address the question. "Look, once we finish the development we're starting, I'm gonna slow down and take you to Bequia and teach you how to hoist a sail."

"Listen, you blow boater," I teased as if blow boater were a derogatory term, "I don't hoist sails. I crank engines. Vroooommmm. Vroooommmm."

Hadn't Alex just admitted that he still thinks of cancer every day? I realized then that he needed a rest, some time to heal before he faced future complications. Was I being fatalistic — or simply realistic? Knowing that he had no intention of helping to "put our affairs in order" at that moment, I teasingly added, "You? Slow down? I *gotta* live to see this."

We changed the subject and talked about how our hopes had changed. Sitting by the same pool a year earlier, we'd made plans for our upcoming developments and hoped for their success. How quickly those grand, self-serving, long-term goals had been dwarfed by smaller, short-term ones. We'd first hoped that the doctors were wrong, and when they weren't, that CVP would succeed. Then that R-CHOP would succeed. That side effects would be minimal. That each blood test and CT scan would yield good results. That a bad day would turn into a good tomorrow. Little hopes, one after another, had saved us from emotional bankruptcy.

Sitting by the same pool a year later, we hoped only that my body would remain healthy and strong. Everything else paled in comparison. But then Alex teased, "Okay, you've had your year off. The roads are going in and you've got 177 houses to sell. Can we pick up where we left off a year ago?"

I groaned and teased back, "Does that mean I really have to go back to work? I kinda liked semi-retirement." Then I added jokingly, "You know, we don't have to wait until we finish the new project. We could go to Bequia in February. And Paris is nice in the spring. And how about St. Petersburg in the summer? And — "

"Betsy, did you just win the lottery? Or just how many houses can you sell by February?"

With a melodramatic sigh and a toss of my head against the lounge chair, I moaned, "Oh, I can't sell any. I'm just too tired. Wake me up when it's time to pack."

"Well, I guess we can't go anywhere since you're so tired." Why did I always back myself into corners?

During a lull in one of our many conversations, I laid back to absorb the sun's warmth and thought about how Alex had coped. We had debated about who had suffered more, and he believed that I did. I disagreed. I'd had a brief preview of the medical world. He'd had none. I'd taken more drugs than a couple of hippies and they'd kept me asleep much of the time, or at least detached from my responsibilities, all of which he'd carried. I'd received treatment and attention while he'd watched helplessly from the sidelines. And I only had to deal with cancer. He had to deal with cancer *and* me.

And cancer had definitely complicated his life. He'd had a business to run and employees who depended on our success to feed their families. He'd had his children Greta and Zan to think about. He couldn't possibly have let himself go down. At the same time, cancer had also forced him into the demanding role of supporting someone who has a major illness, a role no one is ever prepared to play. And yet when I was diagnosed, he responded with every ounce of his energy, better than most people could have. He stopped his life many times in order to help me rescue mine. While everyone else saw my brave and funny face, he bore the brunt of my emotions from their highest highs to their deepest lows, and always, he was my wall against the crush of them.

How he had maintained his composure day after day seemed remarkable. I was amazed that he had found that delicate balance between fighting the battle with me and not being consumed by it. If the roles had been reversed, I seriously doubt I could have managed as well as he did. My emotional survival and ultimate recovery are as much his victory as mine.

But where did all that leave us? It left us hoping that scientists would work around the clock to find cures for me and for every other family whose life is derailed by disease. It left us hoping that Zevalin would work long enough for a curative treatment to become available should I need it. It left us hoping that we would have many good years together even as we made each day the best that it could be.

On Christmas Day, I handed Alex a small gift which he slowly unwrapped. Inside was the box that once held his ring and a note that read, "Dear Alex, Tomorrow we will go to size your new ring. I love you, Betsy." His bottom and top lips curled inward, and he stared silently at the note for several long moments. Pulling me close, he finally stammered, almost inaudibly, "I'm sorry I lost…I wish…You shouldn't…" Silence again.

"You're welcome. Glad you like it," I spoke for him.

And then he asked, "Could we have the ring inscribed just like the old one?"

The following day we headed to Michael's Jewelers in downtown West Palm Beach where my friends Michael and Murray Sperber were expecting us. I gave them all the necessary artwork to emblazon the coat-of-arms on the ring, and Alex wrote the inscription for engraving on the inside: ESH to ATdeP, 9-6-98. Michael jokingly offered to insert a pin through Alex's finger *and* the ring. Half smiling, Alex turned to me and said, "You just need to stay well so I don't fidget."

I saluted him. "Yes, dear." Neither of us had to say that I had just put one of my affairs in order. And so I added lightly, "Lose it again and *your* life will be in danger."

On December 30th, we were to return to Ann Arbor on a very early morning flight. Packing up the night before, I encouraged Alex to do likewise but he was too busy reading a book. I pressed, "Alex, why don't you take a break and pack up tonight so we won't be rushed in the morning?"

"Don't worry," he mumbled, paying no attention to me.

Absentmindedly I said, "Alex, you're gonna be late for your own funeral."

He started to answer, "Yeah, but…" then stopped, put the book down, and looked horrified.

Before he could say anything, I laughed and finished the sentence for him, "Yeah, I know, I'm gonna be early to mine."

"Betsy, I'm sorry, I didn't mean to…No, you can't be early. I mean…"

"Alex, it's just an expression. We've said it for years. You're always late. I'm always early or at least on time. What's gonna change?"

Grimacing, he suggested, "How about a new expression?"

"Be on time and we won't need one," I bantered with a smile.

Waiting to board the plane the following morning, I was reading *Sunlight At Midnight,* a book about the history of St. Petersburg. Without warning, my eyes flooded with tears and my chin began to quiver. Russian history may have its tragic moments, but it's not *that* tragic, I thought. What was wrong with me? There was that little voice again asking whether or not I would be able to return to Florida for another Christmas. It told me I'd never get to St. Petersburg. This time I shot back, "Don't bet on it. I have lots of frequent flier miles." Trying to stop the tears, I looked up at the ceiling and hated my subconscious for interrupting a perfectly good book, for reminding me of nagging doubts, *and* for doing it in a public place.

Back in Ann Arbor, on January 7, I awakened to a full schedule. I got dressed and put the wig on, then took it off. Screw it, I thought. I'm tired of the damn thing. I scrounged through my vanity, found a can of mousse, squealed with delight when the aerosol valve still worked, spiked my very short hair and left the house, wigless, for the first time in months. Heading up US 23, I passed the Silver Lake exit and thought about Dr. Ketcham's call exactly one year earlier. I smiled as I remembered his response when I'd recently run into him and thanked him for being so thorough. He'd modestly said, "No thanks necessary. I was just doing my job."

In the afternoon, I met a client and our kitchen designer and nearly froze as we laid out the kitchen in the open frame of the house. Heading to meet another client afterwards, tropical music was just what I needed to warm me. I slipped in a Jimmy Buffett CD and idly began humming along, preoccupied with thoughts of my next meeting. Suddenly, Jimmy himself may as well have been sitting in the passenger seat saying, "Hey, listen up. This one's for you, Babe." Loud and clear, he sang out, "Yesterday's over my shoulder, so I can't look back for too long. There's just so much to see waiting in front of me that I know that I just can't go wrong...With these changes in latitude, changes in attitude, nothin' remains quite the same..."

Y-e-e-e-s-s-s! *There's just so much to see waiting in front of me!* I replayed that part of the song over and over again — for months. Neither chemo nor RIT had improved my vocal skills, but every time Jimmy sang, "There's just so much to see waiting in front in me," I bellowed out the words with him. They became my mantra. Of course I frequently suggest to Alex that a permanent change in latitude — to Florida — would be nice, too.

Later that day, I reviewed plans for a new house, ordered title work for an impending sale, resisted a strong urge to call Judy and beg her to order a blood test, stopped by the grocery store, filled my car with gas, called Alex three, maybe four times to say "I love you," cooked dinner, watched the news, sewed a button on a shirt and packed a few boxes for our move, just three weeks away. It was a routine day in our life — our *normal* life!

While I was packing boxes in the dining room, Alex wandered in and asked, "You really want to go to St. Petersburg, don't you?"

Without looking up, I answered, "Sure, why?"

"Well, let's plan it. How about sometime in July?"

Astonished, I looked up and asked, "Do you mean it? You'd take off work during the busiest time of year?"

Grinning from ear to ear, Alex replied, "Why not?"

I could scarcely believe Alex's words. I can hardly persuade him to take an hour off from work, much less enough time to travel overseas. For a few moments, I was thrilled, until uncertainty tried to steal my delight. "Alex, that's months from now. What if…"

"Betsy, Dr. Kaminski handed our life back to us. We need to let go of the past year and go on."

"Yes, we do," I smiled. But I still wasn't sure how I would do that.

When Alex and I crawled into bed that night, we read for a few minutes as we do every night. Had he known what day it was? If he had, he hadn't mentioned it, and I decided not to remind him. He kissed me goodnight, turned out the lights and fell asleep quickly.

In the darkness, I wondered if I'd make it to Skye's and Nicholas' college graduations and then mused that they'd hardly notice my presence, busy as they would be with their own friends. But just then, I thought, they were still young enough to play with their old — make that young — grandmother. Pulling the future a little closer and imagining their smiles and giggles, I dreamt of taking them to Disney World soon. There, the adventures are *fun!*

● ● ●

It's not the mountain we conquer but ourselves.
— *Sir Edmund Hillary*

19. | BACK TO THE FUTURE

W hen I completed the last two chapters just days after the first anniversary of my diagnosis, I sounded pretty convincing that I was letting go of cancer and going on, didn't I? The truth is, recovering from treatment doesn't come neatly gift wrapped, nor is it a straight line. Unlike illness, which strikes forcefully and abruptly, recovery comes slowly and subtly. And just what is recovery? To me, it meant that having the ability to enjoy life's pleasures again even with uncertainty as my constant companion. And I would discover that recovery takes time, effort and patience. Lots of patience.

Physically, it took nearly six months after treatment for my energy level to recover to where it had been when I was diagnosed. After that, I felt better and better. Nine months after treatment, I was peppier than I had been in several years, and by then, people who hadn't seen me in some time commented that I looked better than ever. In retrospect, cancer had been eating away at me for a long time, so slowly and subtly that no one noticed, not even me.

Yes, side effects faded, energy returned and hair grew back, but just because there was no outward sign of illness didn't mean that I had recovered. On the contrary, illness lingered beneath the surface for several long months, and gremlins of doubt often tripped me up along the path to recovery. They'd land on my shoulder and whisper in my ear, "Ha, ha, you may be well now, but every healthy day puts you one day closer to returning to Cancer Land." I would reply, "Yes, I *am* well now and every day puts me one day farther *away* from Cancer Land. I have no intention of returning." But believing it was much harder than saying it, and I spent considerable time and effort consciously, furiously fighting off the gremlins that cancer left in its wake.

And as much as I fought to jump right back into my old life, I didn't. Hard as I looked, I couldn't find it. Several months would pass before I would realize that my old life, as I once knew it, was long gone and that I could neither retrieve what was in the past nor move forward while looking backwards. As I gradually began to look ahead, I glimpsed large remnants of my old life rearranged and emerging into a new life. You see, cancer sends you on a slightly different path. It strips away everything but what is most important and leaves you learning how to let go of what is unimportant and how to hold on to what is. But that's easier said than done.

One step at a time, I returned to most of my old activities, at least the ones to which I wanted to return. And I found some new interests. I learned to make commitments a week ahead, then two, then three. Making them four weeks out was harder, but I forced myself to make them so long as they kept me close to home. I was perfectly happy to travel in the states, and I did. I had no problem jumping on a plane to visit the grandbabies in Florida and my mother and sister in Virginia.

The thought of traveling overseas, however, was daunting, and I made all kinds of excuses to postpone making arrangements for our St. Petersburg trip. The simple truth is that July, in January, seemed a lifetime away. In February and March, it didn't seem any closer. And what if I relapsed in Russia? The only Russian words I knew meant hello, goodbye, and son of a bitch — not exactly useful if I had to communicate with a Russian doctor.

CT scans, blood work and physical inspections at three month intervals confirmed that I was achieving deep remission and that I could reasonably expect RIT to continue doing its job for longer than two years. Even with that good news, I was still haunted by the six and ten month execution dates that Dr. Doom had set for me. Intellectually, I knew better than to let mere words plague me, but they sometimes did, no matter how hard I fought back. March 11, six months after RIT, came and went uneventfully, and I breathed a sigh of relief, but I still kept myself tethered close enough to Ann Arbor where I could get help quickly if I needed it.

On the first warm spring day, I ventured into the garden for the first time in nearly two years, and the dirtier I got, the happier I was. When Alex pulled into the driveway late in the afternoon, he stopped near where I was working and leaned out the window. I shivered at the sight of the unadulterated, unabashed smile spread across his face. I remembered that smile. It was the one he reserved for something that particularly pleased him. Realizing how long it had been since I had seen it, my eyes grew a little watery. Alex leaped out of his truck and walked briskly over to scoop me up in his arms. "Boy, is it good to see you out here," he said.

"Ah, yes," I flirted, pulling away and patting his cheeks with clay stained hands. "Your very dirty, very healthy girlfriend has spent a delightful day playing in the spores."

I was overjoyed to see that Alex was better. At last, his droopy shoulders had straightened. His eyes lit up, and he smiled his genteel smile much more easily. No permanent lines remained from months of furrowing his eyebrows. And he no longer fidgeted with his wedding ring. I can't say that cancer made him stop to smell the roses, but he occasionally sniffed a petal or two. Mostly, he was back in full workaholic swing and sometimes forgot that the company would survive if we stepped out on an occasional weeknight. Of course I considered it my wifely duty to remind him, and he smiled sheepishly when I did.

By early May, I cautiously investigated airline tickets and accommodations in St. Petersburg. The city was celebrating its 300th anniversary that summer, and hotels had been booked for months. What remained was sky high, and the price of tickets had doubled since I had first checked in January. Our trip to St. Petersburg was out. My disappointment was offset by relief — there were still two months left before the second execution date.

In June, the FDA finally approved Bexxar, thirteen years after the first clinical trials. Hooray! I have no idea whether Dr. Kaminski took time out to celebrate his own achievement, but one thing I do know. He's not one to rest on his laurels. To this day, he continues to study Bexxar, and the results of his studies continue to get better and better.

That same month, Alex and I began to consider an alternate overseas trip for September. We searched the web and found reasonable airline tickets and hotel accommodations. Would I buy them? Nope. Not until I woke up breathing after ten months.

Four days before that anniversary, another CT scan proved that I was just fine. I finally asked Dr. Kaminski if it was safe for us to travel overseas. He thought it was a splendid idea and assured me that I did not need to pack a suitcase full of drugs "just in case."

On July 11, 2003, exactly ten months after Zevalin, I took a deep breath as Alex and I bought our plane tickets, feeling cautiously free at last to *really* let go and go on. And mostly, I did. Yes, I know it seems ridiculous that a few words took such hold of me, and I'm a little ashamed that I was unable to cast them off as the bunk that they were, but cancer wounds are deep, and words, even when you do your best to cast them off, can keep those deep wounds festering.

Also in July, a year after my last chemo treatment, I was sitting at a stoplight and turned my head quickly to read a sign. Did I feel my hair move? Cautiously, I shook my head from side to side. Y-e-e-e-s-s-s-s!!! It moved! Barely. But I did feel soft wisps brushing the back of my neck! What a marvelous accessory to good health!

The light turned green, and I sped off, wildly shimmying my head back and forth, laughing and singing, "There's just so much to see waiting in front of me..." I really didn't care if neighboring drivers thought I was crazy. In fact, I wanted to shout out the window, "Hallelujah! My hair moves! I'm *normal!*"

We met with Dr. Kaminski on September 22, one year and eleven days past Zevalin. I'd reached a huge milestone, he happily reported. A clear CT scan and perfect bloodwork confirmed *complete* remission. And having achieved that blissful state for a whole year, statistics indicated that I could reasonably expect a five year reprieve — or longer — provided Zevalin did what Bexxar was known to do. Better yet, if lymphoma were to strike again, I wasn't necessarily facing more chemo or a bone marrow transplant. Depending on how it returned, *if* it did, I could take Bexxar. That news raised the sword of Damocles much higher. Dr. Kaminski, Judy and I hugged as we said goodbye that day. They were clearly as pleased with my progress as I was.

The following day, Alex and I left work and responsibilities behind for twelve glorious days. Stepping on to the plane was a giant leap of faith that I could trust my body to cooperate without the safety net of nearby doctors. We flew to Warsaw where we spent a single night on our way to Lviv, from whence we headed to Krakow, Prague and points in between. That first night away, under a clear, star-studded Warsaw sky, we strolled the Old Town Square hand in hand. For awhile, we walked in silence. Suddenly, Alex pulled me very close and whispered, "This time last year, did you think we'd ever have a trip like this?"

My eyes filled with tears, and I could barely whisper back, "No." There in the square, surrounded by natives and tourists and lively accordions, two crazy-with-joy Americans stood holding each other, thanking God and Dr. Kaminski and Judy and all of our friends and family. At that moment, I think we finally exhaled after taking deep breaths and holding them for a very long time. I so wanted to believe that our happily-ever-after life could at last resume. And mostly, it did.

As the immediate terror of cancer diminished, day to day life really did return to normal in almost every way. I gradually began to answer "Fine" to "How are you?" without wondering if I really was or if the person asking was probing about my health. Occasionally, someone would raise an eyebrow and ask, "No, *really*, how *are* you?" and I would realize they wanted to know if I still had cancer. Most of the time, I grinned and made some wisecrack like, "If you're wondering if I'm planning to do lymphoma again, no. Let's do lunch instead."

Little by little, I settled comfortably into my old job, not because I felt guilty about the workload on Alex, but because I genuinely enjoyed it. And because I was extraordinarily glad that I could. Sure, I had occasional delusions about chucking it all and living on a boat in the Caribbean, but my checkbook would have screamed, "You're hallucinating." And how could I possibly have passed up the opportunity to reclaim one of the largest fragments of my old life, especially when I so desperately needed to replace fear and doubt with purpose and passion?

And it felt good to be working with Alex again. The line between our personal and professional lives will always be hopelessly blurred, but our relationship succeeds because we are both equally committed to it, because we both enjoy what we do more than we dislike its inherent challenges, and because we find interludes for fun. And more than ever before, we found how much each of us completes the other.

Gradually, Alex and I realized that we were still the same people we were before cancer invaded our lives except that cancer had become part of who we are, and we began to look at life through a different lens. Yes, cancer changed our view of the world. Staring at death gave us a heightened appreciation for life. It challenged us to live fully the life that we have and forced us to pay attention to the present moment, which is all we really have and all that really matters. And our new perspective gives us more contentment, more joy, more compassion, more empathy.

My mother, of course, continued to be a source of inspiration. On Christmas Day 2003, I took a very early flight to Virginia that arrived by the time she was getting up. Karen and I hadn't told her I was coming, and was she ever surprised! As I left to return home, Mother said, "I hope you didn't come to visit me because you thought this was going to be my last Christmas. I'll be around next year, and I'm going to expect you back." I laughed and thought, "Not only did you give me your longevity genes, you taught me the power of hope." At 94, she was living proof that no one can predict the length of life.

My mother's heart finally gave out on August 28, 2005, less than a month before her 96th birthday. The original edition of this book had come out the previous February, and I'd vacillated about whether or not to give her a copy. Knowing that she would be proud, I decided to write her a letter explaining my illness and why Karen and I had never told her about it. Indeed, she was proud of the book, but proving that you can never fool a mother, she also responded that she had imagined much worse than the truth. Shame on me for not realizing that trying to protect my mother only caused her additional worry. The truth was a relief to her, and I think she passed away more comfortably believing that I was fine.

By then, the homebuilding business was booming, and Alex and I had little time for anything but work. My story was published, the book would speak for me, and I hoped that it would provide insight and inspiration for those who followed in my footsteps. Except for helping with an annual fundraiser for U of M, I'd left Cancer Land behind. Little did I know how quickly I would return for whole new adventures.

●　●　●

Never doubt that a small group of thoughtful, committed people can change the world. Indeed, it is the only thing that ever has.
— *Margaret Mead*

20. | RE-MISSIONED

It's not that I no longer thought of cancer. I did. But it wasn't the first thing I thought of in the morning nor the last thing I thought of at night. Still, I was fully aware that I could wake up one day to begin the whole cycle of illness and treatment again, but as long as I was living and breathing, it seemed to me that I should focus on squeezing out the pleasures of life and family and friends and work and play — which is why I was perfectly happy to live my life without additional reminders of cancer.

But in remission, my life was re-missioned when I learned that profit and politics were taking precedence over cancer patients. How could I turn my back? I couldn't. I got drawn into fighting for the very same treatment that had saved me. And much more.

When I took RIT in 2002, Alex and I had assumed that it would take its rightful place among the smorgasbord of treatment options. After all, if given a choice, who wouldn't prefer a treatment that takes two weeks, has fewer side effects than chemo and, according to studies, is more effective? What's not to love, at least as far as cancer treatment goes? So why, after the first edition of this book came out in 2005, was I hearing from person after person that they'd never heard of RIT or that their doctors dismissed it when asked? I couldn't imagine.

A year later, I finally mentioned my concern to Alex who, without blinking, said, "Follow the money." What? Was he really saying that money influences medical decisions? Surely he was kidding. Call me Pollyanna.

I set out to prove Alex wrong. Turning myself into an investigative reporter, I contacted many people across the country, including several doctors. Most were perfectly willing to discuss why RIT was underutilized, but only off the record. They all explained that oncologists must refer their patients to nuclear medicine physicians or radiation oncologists for administration of RIT, which of course I knew. I'd seen the process up close and personal. What was the problem?

I learned that chemotherapy provides an important revenue stream for oncologists who are in private practice. Essentially, they "buy" the drugs wholesale and "sell" them retail. Thus, when they refer patients to others for administration of RIT, they lose the income from drugs they can administer — namely, chemo and Rituxan, which is what most oncologists kept right on using because there is no standard of care for certain types of lymphoma and because it helped to support their practices. Doctors at universities, I learned, are salaried so they don't have that financial conflict, but their tenure is often tied to their ability to secure grants, and grants fund research in their own areas of interest, which means they could be influenced by the need to accrue patients for their own studies. That was much more than I ever wanted to know.

I also learned that only 5% to 10% of the patients eligible for RIT had actually gotten it in any given year since its approval, even though studies had shown it to be a very effective treatment. Obviously, it had not taken an equal place among the smorgasbord of treatment options because RIT didn't compete with the earning power of chemo and Rituxan.

If this was bad for lymphoma patients, the bigger picture was worse. Person after person voiced concern that interest in developing radioimmunotherapy treatments for other types of cancer — and even other diseases — appeared to be waning because Bexxar and Zevalin had not blazed a successful commercial trail for other drugs in this class of medicine. It was therefore unlikely that companies would take the risk to develop future radioimmunotherapy drugs. For cancer patients, promising new treatments might be delayed or even halted.

Much to my dismay, Alex had been right. For three months, I'd followed the money and found that profit apparently took precedence over people. And RIT wasn't the only example about which I learned. I'd never given much thought to the fact that medicine is, in fact, a multi-billion dollar a year industry, and confronting the business side of medicine took a big bite out of Pollyanna.

More than that, I hated the thought that people who would follow in my footsteps might be so naïve as I, especially when making important medical choices. And I shuddered to think where I might be if I'd had a doctor who didn't use RIT or one who was willing to refer me to a doctor who did. Most probably, pushing up daisies. It just seemed to me that everyone — with every kind of disease — deserves to know all their options and that financial incentives shouldn't come into play when somebody's life is on the line.

Surely, this was a scoop for someone in the national media. Right? Wrong. I contacted reporter after reporter, but most blew me off. And the hierarchy in the cancer world raised its ugly head when some said to me, "If this were a breast cancer treatment, there would be a story." One had the gall to add, "Lymphoma's just not sexy." Seething on the inside, I lightly, and most probably sarcastically, shot back, "Well, next time I'll try to get a sexy cancer." Nobody seemed to grasp that this wasn't about lymphoma, but about a major flaw in the medical system — that is, until all drugs are paid for equally, some don't stand a chance no matter how many lives they might save.

And it wasn't as if RIT was grossly out of line with other cancer treatments. In fact, the total cost of my RIT treatment, including the drugs and the appointments with Dr. Doom and all the tests at the other hospital, totaled $36,929. Compare that to the cost of everything that didn't work: $162,410! And remember — I never finished a single chemo treatment! What would the cost have been if I had? If anyone seriously wanted to reduce the burden of health care costs, RIT could certainly help.

While I was hitting brick walls with the national press, a story entitled "Users Fear That Lymphoma Drugs Will Disappear" showed up in the prestigious *Journal of the National Cancer Institute* in April 2007. It said, "RIT is far from ideal for the medical oncologists (who) must refer patients to radiation oncologists or nuclear medicine specialists and then coordinate treatment. This involves more effort…and it means less money…so RIT, viewed from the standpoint of the medical oncologist's convenience and financial compensation, has problems." Well, excuse me, but lymphoma, when viewed from the standpoint of patients, is pretty inconvenient, too, and in my humble opinion, the value of our lives should trump anyone's compensation.

It was an eye-opening story, but who reads the *Journal?* Mostly doctors or people in the medical field. I hoped it would give them pause, but the story would not likely reach patients.

Finally, in July 2007, the *New York Times* broke the story — on the front page, no less. The headline read: "Market Forces Cited in Lymphoma Drug's Disuse." Needless to say, the *New York Times* didn't take my word for this unfortunate mess. They did their own research and came to the same conclusion, stating that "The reasons that more patients don't get these drugs reflect the market driven forces that can distort medical decisions," and "…that cancer doctors, or oncologists, have financial incentives to use drugs other than Bexxar and Zevalin, which they are not paid to administer." For the first time, oncologists were quoted, and I admired them greatly for speaking out on behalf of patients.

The article circulated far and wide throughout the lymphoma community, and I thought: mission accomplished. Patients who have never heard of RIT will ask their doctors. Patients with all kinds of illnesses will dig a little deeper to make sure that they know all their options. And I went back to my busy world of real estate. Done.

Five months later, I found out that RIT had another problem: it was about to become medical history. I had never heard of the Centers for Medicare and Medicaid Services (CMS), so I could not have known that each year CMS releases its Medicare payment rates for the following year for every drug, medical service and procedure known to man or woman and that private insurance companies usually base their reimbursements on CMS rates. CMS also prohibits hospitals from offering treatments to privately insured patients unless they also offer them to Medicare patients. In other words, hospitals either offer treatments to everyone or to no one.

On November 1, 2007, CMS released its Final Ruling with rates that would take effect on January 1, 2008. Payment for both Bexxar and Zevalin was to be slashed to about half their cost — not because the drugs weren't effective, but by CMS' own admission, because of known errors in accounting methodology. This gave hospitals a choice: they could provide the treatment to everyone and lose thousands of dollars per dose or offer it to no one. Never mind the cost of human life. Which do you think they would choose? Even a bureaucrat should be able to figure that out.

But none of this changed the fact that there was only a two-month window to correct this blunder. Once the rates went into effect on January 1, they could not be overturned by any means. And if reimbursement was only half the cost, the chance of any doctor or hospital using RIT, already underutilized, was virtually zilch. The very treatment that had rescued me from death was itself about to die, and there was no way I was going to let that happen without a fight. In the bigger picture, I believed that we patients deserve to have every treatment option available, regardless of what it is.

Very quickly, I learned that CMS cannot reverse any part of its own Final Ruling. Only the United States Congress has that power. Well, now, that was a problem. I didn't happen to have any members of Congress on speed dial — not even the lowliest staffer — but I was determined to find an ally who could make a lot more noise than I could. Through a fellow lymphoma survivor and colleague of Jonathan Alter — himself a lymphoma survivor and then *Newsweek's* Senior Editor — Jonathan and I connected by email. He was open to learning more about the problem, but like all good journalists, he did his own research far beyond what any one of us told him. Still, no promises were made about whether an article would or wouldn't be published. I held my breath.

Thirteen days after the ruling came out, "How Washington Is Nixing A Cancer Cure" threw a hard punch. Jonathan began, "What if they found a cure for cancer that afflicts half a million people, but a combination of stupid bureaucrats and greedy doctors kept patients from getting it? It's the kind of scenario that seems like the province of conspiracy theorists or alternative-medicine wackos — but is actually happening right now with a proven treatment for certain types of non-Hodgkin lymphoma."

Wow! As I read the story, tears welled in my eyes and I could hardly believe what I was reading — in *Newsweek* no less! Jonathan quoted experts, including Dr. Bruce Cheson of Georgetown University Hospital, who said, "RIT is the most effective, least used treatment in oncology." Mind you, Dr. Cheson didn't say it's the least used treatment in lymphoma, but the most effective, least used treatment in *all* of oncology. And Dr. Andrew Schafer, then president of the American Society of Hematology, said that RIT may be the *only* treatment option for some patients. In those cases, Jonathan concluded that without it, "the patients die." I couldn't have known how prophetic his words would be.

I quickly found out that scathing press can open doors in Washington. Two days after the article came out, my own senator from Michigan, The Honorable Debbie Stabenow, took up the cause. I never talked with Senator Stabenow directly, but her senior health aide assured me that the senator would take the lead and do everything she could to get the necessary support to overturn the ruling. And she did.

But surely Senator Stabenow needed help — right? With the deadline looming, I turned my complete attention to trying to get the ruling overturned — not that I had any idea how to do it. Once again, Alex pulled my weight and gave me the time to do whatever I could. He knew as well as I did that someday, somewhere, someone might benefit from RIT, just as we had, and we shuddered to think that it wouldn't be around for another person who might need it. Doing nothing was not even an option because the consequences of losing RIT were too dire.

A friend and I put out the word on lymphoma forums, started a petition which garnered more than 4,000 signatures, and asked people to contact their representatives. The effort snowballed into so many calls and emails to Congress that the senior health aide for the Finance Committee sent me an email saying, "We hear you. We're doing everything we can." Not good enough! We wanted a fix!

And we weren't alone. Individual doctors and organizations were contacting Congress, too, but Congress was in the midst of fighting over appropriations for the entire federal budget. RIT wasn't even a whole drop in that big bucket so a lot of ruckus had to be made. And it was. A tiny little paragraph directing CMS to fully reimburse for RIT was finally inserted into the huge Medicare bill. The language didn't quite get full reimbursement, but it was good enough to save RIT so that the details could be worked out later. Getting doctors to use it would be a whole 'nother issue, but at least it would still be around.

The usual Washington political antics were just as much in play then, under President Bush, as they are as I write this today. It wasn't pretty. I wanted to scream, "Quit bickering and get busy!" Political ideology was taking precedence over people who were sick, for goodness sakes, and I kept thinking, "Geez, this isn't political. It's cancer. And neither side is immune." Politicizing a disease was, to me, unconscionable, and another piece of Pollyanna succumbed to the reality of partisan politics.

The vote was scheduled for December 19, 2007, the very day that I was flying to Florida for the holidays. I enlisted a friend to watch C-Span for me and had just put my bag on the conveyor belt at airport security when he called. I grabbed my bag and stood aside, amidst "oh-how-can-you-be-so-rude" stares. I didn't care. That call was far more important than the manners my mother taught me.

Excitedly, my friend blurted out, "The bill passed. Once Bush puts his signature on it, RIT is saved." His words turned on the waterworks. I'm sure I was grinning from ear to ear, but tears spilled down my cheeks, and all I could manage to say, repeatedly, was "Thank God, I can't believe it. Thank God, I can't believe it."

I really tried to whisper and to be as unobtrusive as possible, but when I looked up, I saw that several people had frozen to watch the conversation, and there I was laughing and crying at the same time. I was so embarrassed. To the puzzled faces who seemed to want an explanation, I simply said, "Congress just passed a bill that saved a great cancer treatment from extinction." A couple of people smiled. Most just returned to the task of getting through security.

And then I wondered if I would. Losing your composure at airport security is not the best thing to do, and I feared that the guards would see me as some hysterical woman and haul me off as an emotionally unstable passenger, but they couldn't have been nicer. In fact, every one of them patted me on the back. Tears were still falling down my cheeks all the way through security, but I was smiling broadly. And I didn't need a plane to put me in the clouds. The news had already put me way above them.

Settling into my seat, I suddenly realized how utterly exhausted I was, but sleep never came on the three hour flight. Relieved and happy, I thought about the many people who had joined the effort to save RIT, how glad I was to have been one of them, and how relieved I was that it would still be available to anyone who needed it. The next day, I lost my voice completely for three days. Too bad Alex was still in Michigan. He's never known such silence.

● ● ●

There is only one thing more painful than learning from experience,
and that is not learning from experience.
— *Archibald MacLeish*

21. | THE CRUELEST IRONY

Just three months before the CMS fiasco began, my in-laws, Lisa
and Ted, moved to a small town in Florida to permanently
escape the cold Michigan winters. Alex's sister lived nearby.
Though up in years, they were, physically and mentally, much
younger than their chronological ages. In fact, they'd never been sick
a day in their lives and continued to walk miles every day, swim,
dance, and hold lively conversations on a wide variety of topics. Lisa,
in fact, outdanced Alex at her 90th birthday party in April 2008.
What happened to her next is a painful cautionary tale, shared —
with Alex's blessing — for the many lessons it can teach.

In May, a month after her birthday party, Lisa got sick. For the
next three months, she was passed from one doctor to another and
underwent test after inconclusive test. In June, a CT showed masses
that were suspected to be lymphoma or pancreatic cancer. Despite
no definitive diagnosis, doctors prescribed a variety of medications
which, not surprisingly, didn't reduce her symptoms.

Alex and I grew increasingly concerned. Living through lymphoma, we'd learned a thing or two, and we knew that a CT scan
determines where a mass is located, but that only a biopsy can determine what type of mass it is. A diagnosis, much less a treatment plan,

couldn't be reached through guesswork, and prescribing medications based on guesswork seemed less than logical, to put it mildly.

By early August, Lisa was in the care of a general oncologist — one who treats all kinds of cancers — and she had undergone two fine needle aspirations (FNA), procedures which draw cells from a suspicious area using a long, thin needle. Alex and I knew that FNA's are not generally suitable for the diagnosis of lymphoma because they can't generally extract enough material to make a diagnosis, so we weren't surprised when the results came back inconclusive.

One report stated that her tissue was "highly suspicious for lymphoma." Another narrowed it down to "B-cell lymphoma." Big whoop. About 85% of lymphomas are B cell lymphomas, but there are many types, and treatment isn't the same for all. Three months after Lisa's symptoms started — and were getting worse — all we had was B-cell lymphoma.

By that time, Alex and I were beside ourselves. We had been begging Lisa to return to Michigan, if only for a second opinion, but she did what so many patients do when they're diagnosed: uncharacteristically, she put all her faith in her one doctor.

We'd never known Lisa to hesitate to question anybody about anything. She was bright, well-educated and curious. Born and raised in Germany, she lived through the horrors of World War II. Just days after the British and Americans bombed Dresden in 1945, she slept in the rubble while trying to make her way back to her parents' home, although she never made it. Instead, with the Russians marching toward Berlin, she quickly married Ted whom she had known for just six weeks. Both feared that Russian "liberation" was a thin disguise for "domination." If their suspicions were right, which history proved them to be, they knew that their very survival depended on escape from Russian territory because Ted had been a Ukrainian freedom-fighter and the Russians would have killed him. Only with their own cunning and courage, plus sheer luck, were they able to slip into the safety of the U.S. zone. From there, they fled to Paris where Alex was born and later immigrated to America where Paradowsky became de Parry. These events in Lisa's early life shaped her and made her one of the strongest women I have ever known.

But illness was sapping her strength. Her doctor was nice, she said, and she didn't want to leave Ted to come to Michigan, although he could certainly have come with her. Alex and I reminded her that she had witnessed my illness and the care that I'd had on an almost daily basis, and she certainly knew that I would probably be dead if I hadn't been in the care of a lymphoma specialist. She also knew all about the underutilization of RIT and the recent CMS issue.

But knowing something intellectually and acting on it are sometimes two different things, especially when we don't feel well enough to act. And Lisa wasn't feeling well at all, though she tried to maintain a brave face to minimize everyone's worry. At least she never once tried to fool me. In fact, she always told me that I was the one person in whom she could confide because she knew that I would understand, and we had many intimate, no-holds-barred conversations.

I was always as honest with Lisa as she was with me. When she would tell me that her goal was to outlive Ted, I would tell her that she had a role to play in achieving that goal, namely, getting a second opinion so that she could be correctly diagnosed and properly treated. I reminded her that the field of cancer is changing rapidly. That it is humanly impossible for any one doctor to keep up with all the changes. That specialists are much more on top of the latest advances. And that just as experience and knowledge matters in everything, it especially matters when our lives are at stake. I even asked her, "Would you take a Ferrari to a general mechanic?" She agreed that she wouldn't. But the physical effects of her illness were draining her usual spirit and leading her down the path of least resistance. How well I understood how easily that can happen.

And therein lies a dilemma. Emotionally, our doctors are our lifelines. In the throes of illness, the last thing we want to do is suspect that our lifelines are not as strong as they could be. We patients must have faith and confidence in the people who are treating us. Even if we're well-informed, they are the experts, and many of us will only go so far in questioning their recommendations, if we question them at all.

Alex and I both understood that, and we repeatedly tried to be Lisa's strength. Time and time again, we tried to assure her that if she would just come for a second opinion, Michigan doctors would coordinate her care with her Florida doctor and she could return to Florida for treatment, but with extra, expert eyes looking out for her and with more confidence in a treatment plan. Every time we thought she was convinced, she backed off. And if you've ever tried to change the mind of a strong-willed German matriarch, you know that the odds are against you.

But there was something else at work: family dynamics and distance. Alex's sister was there every day and mostly, we were in Michigan, talking with Lisa by phone. His sister, every bit as strong-willed as her mother, knew the local doctors personally, and she contended that they were just as experienced and knowledgeable as the specialists at Michigan or any other major facility. Oh please. Just because someone is a fellow Rotarian doesn't make him a medical specialist. To no avail, we sent paper after paper, study after study, article after article. Not one was authored by one of her doctor friends.

Short of kidnapping Lisa, which would have been impossible, we simply could not get her to see a specialist at Michigan or anywhere else, so we sent her records to one, and he told us what we already knew: that an excisional biopsy — one that yields enough tissue to make identifying the cancer type possible — was necessary if ever a correct diagnosis were to be made. He also said that Lisa had an easily accessible node in her armpit. Of course we relayed all this to Lisa's doctor but the surgeon who finally performed an excisional biopsy chose instead to slash into a node in her abdomen, an area from which recovery was much more painful.

And what did it yield? A report stating that her tissue was "best classified as follicular lymphoma with at least Grade II features." Best classified? At least grade II features? Weren't they sure? My biopsy report was much more detailed and certainly more definitive because my tissue was reviewed by pathology specialists. And from the moment I met Dr. Kaminski and lymphoma was suspected, a CT and an excisional biopsy were scheduled, performed and reported within two weeks. In Lisa's case, it had taken nearly four months and several unnecessary tests just to reach a conclusion that wasn't 100% definitive.

Despite what we considered a less than stellar report, it gave Lisa's doctor the tool he needed for a treatment plan: four rounds of Rituxan. She was too "old" for chemotherapy, and he wouldn't even discuss RIT, even though it's recommended as an appropriate treatment for elderly patients. As you might also guess, RIT was not available at the hospital where he practiced.

Lisa was comfortable with the plan. She'd stood her ground and stayed in Florida. Alex and I were beyond frustrated but we had no choice but to respect her decision. There was nothing more that we could do except to hope for the best.

She completed treatment and soon reported that she was pain-free and feeling better. Two months later, we were in Michigan when we were told that her followup tests looked fine. Great. Who can argue with success?

Over the Christmas holidays, Lisa was active, happy, glad to see everybody and looked better than she had in months. A month later, her pain and fever returned. Alex's sister called in Hospice on the oncologist's recommendation.

Alex and I hightailed it to Florida. Lisa was nearly unable to eat and was sleeping most of the time because the doctor had prescribed morphine for pain. And he'd prescribed an antibiotic for the fever because he assumed she had an infection, though he had neither examined her nor run any test on which to base the assumption.

We'd been down the path of assumption with Dr. Doom and knew all too well that assumptions are not particularly helpful.

In Lisa's waking moments, she made it very clear that she did not want to sleep all the time. That she'd rather endure some pain and be awake to participate in life. And more than anything, that she wanted to live.

Alex and I suspected that lymphoma, not an infection, was causing the fever. We suggested that Decadron — the same steroid that Dr. Kaminski had prescribed for me when I had relapsed — might reduce the fever, but her doctor and Hospice balked because Decadron is considered a treatment for disease, and Hospice only allows medications to treat symptoms, not the disease itself. After much wrangling, Lisa was on Decadron, the fever stopped within 24 hours, and Hospice bowed out. The morphine was history, too, and Lisa was happier because she could stay awake more. Her appetite even began to improve — not a lot, but it was heading in a better direction.

Again, Alex asked the doctor about RIT and again, he wouldn't discuss it. Instead, he gave Lisa two choices: she could have more Rituxan or she could let nature take its course. His words. Nice, huh? Studies showed that additional Rituxan would be even less likely to work the second time, and Lisa was adamant that letting nature take its course was unacceptable. She finally realized that her very life was at stake and her will to live kicked into overdrive. At last, she agreed to see a specialist, but weak and symptomatic, she couldn't make the trip to Michigan.

Alex gathered all her records, which shouldn't have taken several days to obtain, but did. Again we sent copies to a specialist for review. I spent half the night putting our copies in chronological order and reading them as best as I could. When I came to the CT report from November, two months after treatment, it was very easy to read "continued presence of mass." My stomach knotted and a hot sensation slowly traveled from my head downward all the way to my feet, as if my blood were boiling. We'd been told that Lisa's followup tests looked fine, but we'd never seen the report. And the most recent CT, a couple of weeks earlier, showed that Lisa's nodes had "dramatically increased in size" since November.

The consulting specialist suggested that RIT was probably Lisa's best option but that she needed to be examined by a specialist to confirm. It wasn't until we convinced Lisa's doctor to call our consultant — which he did only reluctantly — that he finally agreed to "release" Lisa to a specialist. Guess what. Doctors don't own patients, and ego and arrogance have no place in medical care.

Not surprisingly, Lisa's doctor did nothing to help us find a specialist. Fortunately, we knew how to go about it and had already started looking, but despite our best efforts, it still took nearly two weeks to get an appointment.

During that time, our worry factor, on a scale of one to ten, was somewhere about a thousand. Lisa worried, too, but not about herself. She worried about Ted. For 64 years, she'd lovingly taken care of him, and she wanted to continue. And as best she could, that's what she did. She laid out his clothes in the mornings and made sure he had tea when he wanted it. She tried to do as much as she could, but asked for help when she needed it — such as, when she wanted to make cucumber salad, she asked me to slice the cucumbers, but she immediately took over when I wasn't slicing them thin enough to suit her. Always the family matriarch, Lisa was bossing us around again, and it was music to our ears.

On Friday, February 27, 2009, Alex finally got his mother to the closest specialist. Although he rarely used RIT and thought my response to it was just "lucky," he did say that Bexxar was Lisa's best option and that she needed it immediately.

The doctor, in fact, performed the requisite bone marrow biopsy to determine whether Lisa could take RIT. At first glance, the pathologist believed that she could. If confirmed on Monday, which it was, the first dose would be ordered and then administered by the end of the following week. We breathed an enormous sigh of relief.

That night, Alex and I were so hopeful. It had seemed such a cruel irony that Lisa had the same disease that I had and that we were living through lymphoma again. For Alex, it must have been even worse — first his wife and then his mother. And it seemed an even stranger twist of fate that his own mother could possibly be rescued by the same treatment that, just over a year earlier, so many of us had worked so hard to save from CMS. Who could ever have imagined that Bexxar would soon become her best chance? No one could possibly have written that script, but we were so grateful to everyone who had pitched in and kept it available.

Around 8:30 the next morning, Lisa stopped breathing. Within minutes, she was in an ambulance racing to the hospital, but she never made it. The official cause of death on her death certificate is cardiac arrest, noting that B-cell lymphoma was a "significant condition contributing to death." No words can begin to express our anguish.

The pain of losing Lisa was — and is — worsened many fold by the fact that even knowing all that we know, we still failed to rescue her from a system that failed her, and we are left with countless what-ifs — among them, what if we had done something differently and what could that have been? What if the doctors had been better equipped to diagnose earlier and quicker? What if her doctor had reacted when the scan in November showed continued presence of masses? What if, at any step along the way, he and Alex's sister had encouraged Lisa to go to Michigan or to any other specialist for a second opinion? What if her doctor had said, "Just to confirm that we're on the right track, I'd like you to see a specialist"?

Knowing that Lisa had followed every other recommendation he'd made, we're convinced that she would have followed that one, too. It wasn't until it was too late that she and Alex's sister finally realized that placing all their confidence in this one man wasn't in Lisa's best interest.

Even if Lisa is simply dismissed as "old," the fact remains that her diagnosis took far longer than it should have. That in the search for a diagnosis, she underwent many unnecessary tests, some of which were fairly invasive and painful. That her diagnosis was not 100% definitive. That seeing a specialist was discouraged. That all her treatment options were not presented. And the sad fact is that Alex and I knew more about lymphoma and its treatment than her doctor.

We will never know what might have happened if Lisa's care had been different, but there's one thing we know for certain: that she — and we — would have preferred a different ending. Of course we know that the outcome would eventually have been the same, but we will always wonder if it could have been postponed if everything that could have been done had in fact been done. Because it wasn't, we're left with too many what-ifs that compound the pain of loss and make our hearts heavier.

On the morning of Lisa's funeral, Ted sat pensively in his chair, still in his pajamas. Time to dress, I told him. He looked up slowly and said, almost inaudibly, "But I don't know what to wear." Any coat and tie would do, Alex said. "But I don't know which one," he replied. "Lisa always laid out my clothes for me." The sadness in his eyes and the grief on his face tore our hearts to pieces.

● ● ●

Turn your face to the sun and the shadows fall behind you.
— *Maori proverb*

22. | STILL STANDING

When cancer called on January 7, 2002 and I soon learned that the median time from diagnosis to death was eight years, I couldn't have imagined then — much less as my stubborn disease seemed to be fast-tracking me to the short side of it — that I would cross to the far side of the median while making a speech about my experience. But that's what I did on January 7, 2010, exactly eight years after my diagnosis and ten months after Lisa's death.

Part of me wanted to jump for joy. Part of me wanted to forget the speech and simply sing Elton John's song "I'm Still Standing," whose words brilliantly convey my defiance to cancer. Here's part of it:

And did you think you could never win?
Well, look at me, I'm coming back again....
Don't you know I'm still standing better than I ever did
Looking like a true survivor, feeling like a little kid.
I'm still standing after all this time
Picking up the pieces without you on my mind.
I'm still standing, yeah, yeah, yeah.
I'm still standing, yeah, yeah, yeah.

Of course the audience would have run for cover if I'd actually sung since my vocal chords never have improved. And even if I could have pulled it off, it wouldn't have felt right unless Lisa had been still standing with me. Because she wasn't, the day felt bittersweet. I can't even imagine what it felt like for Alex. But I had a pretty good idea when I saw him in the back of the room as I spoke about our experience, his face drawn, re-living the pain. I'm sure he never meant for me to see that face.

Of course we're thrilled that I'm still standing and we both know that Lisa would be happy, too. After all, somebody has to find her son's keys and remind him to smell the roses occasionally — right?

I have, in fact, been standing healthy and strong without further treatment for my "incurable" disease. The only late term effects from RIT are great health and lots of energy. But am I really cured? The last time I asked Dr. Kaminski, around five years after treatment, my medical status was "durable, long-term remission." That's Medicalese for "it takes years to prove that new treatments are curative." A few doctors are, in fact, beginning to whisper that RIT may be curative, but most still say there is no known cure for the type of lymphoma that I had.

I beg to differ. The dictionary definition of cure is "to bring back to health" without adding any specific time period. RIT certainly brought me back to health and enabled me to live life uninterrupted by miserable treatment after treatment. I'd say that's living like I'm cured, wouldn't you? The truth is, I don't know what my next scans will show, but I do know that there is no evidence of disease in my body at the moment. That means I am disease free. Cured. Just for today. And hopefully many tomorrows. One of these days, I'll ask Dr. Kaminski what he thinks. Maybe we won't agree on the terminology, but I know we'd agree that I'm healed.

Indeed, I've lived on after cancer and gotten to experience the joys and sorrows that life hands to us all. Alex and I have reclaimed our future, and I'm pretty sure he's glad that I'm still around. Together, we've gotten to celebrate important milestones, and in between them, to celebrate every plain old ordinary routine day with which we've been blessed. I've not only seen Skye and Nicholas start kindergarten, but Skye is now in junior high and Nicholas isn't far behind. Though our physical distance remains far greater than I'd like, I've still witnessed, among other things, birthdays, Halloween costumes, school reports and their first — and I hope last — stitches. And that's what's important, not the label that shows up in my medical records.

So whether I'm cured, healed, or in complete remission is a matter of semantics. I do know some of Dr. Kaminski's patients who took Bexxar in clinical trials as early as 1996 and who have never had a recurrence. I'd call that cured. Maybe scientists will agree someday.

But a chart stamped "cured" isn't a prerequisite for living a full, happy life. Of course we'd all love a guarantee that cancer will never return, but no such guarantee exists. As long as we're alive, illness is a risk of life itself, and death will always be a certainty. Between now and then, it seems to me that the outcome of my life is more important than the outcome of my illness and that what I do is much more important than worrying about the inevitable. And what I do, among other things, is love my family and feed our cat on demand.

Do I worry about relapse? Mostly, no. I rarely worry about things I can't control, but scans and checkups will probably always trigger a case of the jitters, and it never ceases to amaze me that ration and logic (I have no symptoms) shift so easily to doubt (will I dodge the bullet again?). Invariably, Alex tells me, "You're fine. We have nothing to worry about." Thinking that he isn't a CT scanner, much less a doctor who can read its results, I invariably shoot back, "And you know this how?" It's become an annual exchange between us.

On scan day, I slip back into the gown of patienthood and marvel that scientists have developed treatments that target cancer with laser-like precision, but *still*, the ties on gowns don't match up. I wait my turn in the same room where I waited for my first scan all those years ago, and that's when I jitter the most. I always take a good book but it never gets read because my mind races back to the dark place where cancer all started. Will I get to keep living my life? Or will I have to tell everyone that I have cancer again? I know that it's not worth worrying about what will happen to my stuff after I'm gone because — well, I'll be gone, but still I wonder what will happen to the files full of notes that I've made to write witty stories. And will Juli use my mother's silver and think of her and me?

And then I wait. For good news or bad. Either way, I just want to know. And until I do, life pauses. It's not that I stay home wallowing in self pity. On the contrary, I go about my daily routine and make myself busy — *very* busy — but Alex knows better than to ask me to make any big decisions until I know that it's safe again to buy green bananas. ·

Medical tests will punctuate our lives forever, reminding us of what was and what might be again, and thus I get the jitters. Even though I know that they may be irrational, I've come to accept them as part of having once had cancer, and accepting them takes a lot less work than denying their existence. Thankfully, my jitters never last long. Even after all these years, Judy — still caring as much as ever — calls to let me know the results before I see Dr. Kaminski, and I'm just as grateful as ever that she is still chief angel on earth.

And why haven't I relapsed? It's certainly not because I wanted to live more than anyone else. The fact is, I'll never know, and I have better things to do than to waste time wondering.

Over the years, many people have asked if I believe that my outlook contributed to my healing. There was a time, in the months following treatment, that I might have answered a confident yes. Today, I'm not so sure. Why have we lost friends who were as positive as any people you could ever meet? Why do others not respond to treatment? I think now that I was just lucky enough for a powerful new drug to heal my body. The only thing I can say with any certainty is that my outlook helped me to survive the onslaught of uncertainty and that it helped me to take the necessary steps to improve my chances of a good outcome.

I do feel painfully uncomfortable when someone doesn't respond to treatment as favorably as I did. Survivor's guilt perhaps? No, surviving cancer is not committing an offense. George Carlin had good advice when he said, "Don't take guilt trips. Take a trip to the mall, to the next county or to a foreign country, but not to where guilt is." I feel uncomfortable because I've felt the fear when treatment's not working, and I so want to say or do something to make that someone feel better. And yet I've often felt as lost and inept for words as people did during my illness.

I've never forgotten the fear and suffering that cancer inflicted on my family, and as I've listened to the health care debate over these last few years, I can't help but think about the consequences of cancer or any other major illness on the millions of families who still have little or no access to care. I don't understand why someone can serve one term in Congress and have health care for life while someone who's worked for a lifetime can have little or no coverage. I've met some of these people and their stories are heart-wrenching. I don't know how to solve the health care problems, but it disturbs me deeply that there are very real human beings — mothers, fathers, children — whose very lives depend on real reform that opens the door to getting the care they need.

And reform would include changes that give RIT a chance to be considered equally among the treatment options, based on what's best for the patient, not what's best for oncologists' bottom lines or convenience. For all the effort to save RIT from CMS, the vast majority of patients are still undergoing months of chemo and Rituxan while RIT — a one week treatment — is hardly a blip on the treatment option radar, and for all the wrong reasons.

● ● ●

Putting the experience of cancer into the context of our lives, as we all must do, is an ongoing process. I look back now at what I wrote in Chapter17 — which was written as it happened — and I realize that I was working really, really hard to convince myself that life after treatment would be the same as it was before I was ever diagnosed. Eventually, I quit working so hard to deny that cancer leaves an indelible mark. That life is no more the same after cancer than it is after any other major life-changer. Nope, once in Cancer Land, our view of the world is forever changed, but living with illness or in its shadow can make us stronger and wiser, just as any other challenge in life can.

Cancer gave me the wisdom to accept that none of us is always in control of our lives nor can we always shape our own destinies, much as we'd all like to believe. It also gave me the wisdom to accept that quick, concrete answers and predictable outcomes aren't always possible, much as we all want them. But it also confirmed that impossible is sometimes possible.

And cancer gave me the freedom to savor the present like never before. After all, none of us knows what's around the next bend in life, so why *not* enjoy the moment?

As for the language of cancer, some of it doesn't feel quite right to me. For example, never — not once — have I ever felt that I "fought" or "battled" cancer, as the experience is often described. Rather, I made a series of choices with the hope of extending my life — like, among other things, showing up at the hospital and treating myself to a series of potentially life-saving drugs until one of them worked. That's not fighting or battling. It's choosing the possibility of life over certain death. And that's no different than what we all do every day. We make choices in response to challenges that slip into our lives alongside joy and pleasure.

And then there's "survivor." Some wear the label proudly, and if it works for you, great. It just doesn't work for me. From the very beginning of my illness, I hated being called a survivor. During treatment, I wanted to scream, "Survivor? Don't you get it? I want to do a lot more than just survive!" All these years later, labeling me a survivor rubs me the wrong way. It's like allowing cancer to define me. Why can't I just be Betsy, who has done many things in her life and who once happened to have cancer but who doesn't have it now? Don't get me wrong — I love being a survivor. I just don't like the label.

Do I have a better suggestion? I'd prefer no label at all, but if there must be one, I personally like the word "graduate" because it implies that I learned something, but survivor is so widely accepted that it's the word we're stuck with, whether I like it or not. Of course I understand the necessity of a word or short descriptive phrase to identify the nearly twelve million of us who are living after our diagnoses, but there is no single word or phrase that could possibly apply to so many unique individuals. Since survivor is the universally accepted label, I use it despite my distaste.

I'm not alone. Many have told me they don't like being labeled a survivor any more than I do. Some have said — and I see their point — that they think survivorship has been idealized. That this one event suddenly enlightened us, strengthened us, and turned us into brave heroes and fighters. I don't know about you, but that's far too much for me to live up to. And cancer didn't make me brave. In fact, it showed me that I wasn't as brave as I thought.

Cancer did enlighten me to a wider world and make me much more aware of human suffering. But was cancer the wake up call that so many people say that it is? No. I was neither asleep for the pre-lymphoma years of my life nor did I suddenly have a great revelation that life is precious. I already knew that, and never once did I need a reminder.

Did it help me to prioritize? Yes, becoming acutely aware of my finite time here on earth, I try to prioritize better than I did BC — before cancer — but sometimes the demands of life simply get in the way. The year I want to spend in the Caribbean is a priority, but work needs to be done and bills need to be paid and the Caribbean just has to wait.

Did cancer strengthen me? Every difficult situation leaves an indelible mark, but it's also an opportunity to learn a lot about ourselves, and Alex and I did find inner reserves we never knew we had and grew stronger for having found them. But the fact is, life hands us all plenty of tough situations, and we somehow manage to rise to the occasion and do things we never dreamed we could. Every one of us has strength we never knew we had.

Think about it. If anybody ever told you that you'd voluntarily be poked, prodded, knifed, drugged or radiated — if anybody told you that you could flush catheters, clean ports or give yourself shots — would you think you could? Nearly 12 million of us have, but just because I'm one of them does not make me a fighter or a hero. I didn't fight for my life any harder than anybody else. And I didn't volunteer to have cancer for somebody else, which might have been heroic. I simply got sick, took a lot of horrible drugs for several months, laid around most of the time I was taking them, watched my friends and family worry, and then got well. That's not heroic. It's what life handed us. And sometimes life is messy.

Today, Alex and I are still the same people we were before cancer invaded our lives. Only now, cancer is part of who we are, but it's a long way from the sum total. Of course we're grateful that I survived, and we know that I'm one of the lucky ones because I did, but our personal triumph is tempered by the fact that I've cried at the funerals of too many "survivors," which is why, more than anything else, I dislike the term survivor, as it seems to deny that cancer claims the lives of 1500 Americans day in and day out, year after year. That's 9/11 every two days, and I wonder why we aren't all outraged. And why we haven't won this deadly war on cancer. Only then, can we all fit neatly into the label of survivor.

But this is simply how I feel. If survivor works for you, then wear it proudly. In all aspects of cancer, each of us finds what works best for us. I still like "graduate" because it suggests that I actually learned something in Cancer U. Indeed I did, though the lessons were hard and never once have I been glad that I learned them.

What astounds me most is the science I learned. Don't get me wrong. I wouldn't know a cell if I saw one. And I didn't grow a left brain, despite all the drugs that I took. But now more than ever, I appreciate science, even if it's from a right-brained perspective. And I'm pretty sure that there's a special place in heaven for researchers and scientists like Dr. Kaminski who spend their lives trying to make ours better.

I didn't need to get cancer to learn that all doctors are not created equal, but cancer taught me that really great ones know that healing is not just the result of knowing and prescribing the right medications, but also of giving large doses of assurance and of calming our minds, soothing our souls and holding our hands. Of believing in us when we have trouble believing in ourselves. And of taking the time to establish mutual trust and respect. Great doctors also take the time to teach us how to help them so that they can do their best. And sometimes they drop their shield of self-protection, surely at great pain to themselves. Great doctors care not only *for* us but *about* us. And they *always* put what's best for us ahead of what's best for their egos or bottom lines.

We were extraordinarily lucky to have one of those great doctors. Alex and I will always be grateful to Dr. Kaminski and Judy and their colleagues, not only for the medications they prescribed that healed my body, but also for the care, wisdom and compassion that safeguarded my soul and my spirit. It was the perfect combination that undoubtedly left us as unscarred emotionally as any cancer experience possibly could and that helped us to regain our emotional equilibrium faster than we otherwise could have. If you have one of those great doctors, count your lucky stars.

Cancer taught me a whole lot more that could fill a whole 'nother book. Maybe someday I'll write it, but for now, in no particular order, two dozen things that I learned are:

- That cancer sucks big time a bajillion times over.
- That I'll never know why I got it in the first place but dwelling on why won't change the fact that I did.
- That having cancer was like having a full time job that I neither applied for nor wanted.

- That you can feel great with cancer until chemo starts.
- That you get to know yourself best when you're feeling your worst.
- That some good can come out of everything, but not everything happens for the best.
- That chick flicks can be just as soothing as mind-numbing drugs but…
- That "Praise the Lord and pass the valium" is sometimes the only prayer that will do.
- That laughter is an instant vacation from cancer.
- That being strong doesn't mean you don't cry — it just means you don't get stuck in your tears.
- That if cancer isn't enough of a reason to drop the baggage in our lives, I don't know what is.
- That whoever calls cancer a "gift" has surely not received it.
- That perfect strangers become friends but some friends disappear.
- That the best gifts don't come wrapped.
- That some people make stupid comments but probably don't mean them.
- That really tough decisions have to be made but…
- That implementing those decisions is sometimes tougher.
- That chemo sometimes does a better job on hair than cancer.
- That when people talk about being "touched" by cancer, they have no idea that it's more like getting hit by a sledgehammer.
- That politicians sometimes put political agendas over cancer patients and that thousands of us have better things to do but will raise hell when we have to.
- That knowledge empowers us, but it's more important to have the right knowledge.
- That there's always something to be grateful for.
- That sometimes you have to find a way to sing even when there's no song in your heart.

- That happiness can be found in the dark if we remember to turn on the light.

And there's something else. Everyone's adventures in Cancer Land are difficult, but Alex and I saw some sights that we would not have otherwise seen. We saw that cancer gives context to compassion and kindness, and we saw more of that than we ever thought imaginable. We saw that perfect strangers bond by the shared experience. With many, I've laughed, I've cried, and we've told each other things that even our best friends couldn't understand. And we saw the very best in humanity. Cancer introduced us to remarkable people who showed us so much about the goodness and resilience of human beings, and while I would never have cancer by choice, I wouldn't trade that view of world for anything.

There was a time — in the throes of illness — that I couldn't wait to run away from cancer, never to look back, but coming close to death and being rescued in the nick of time leaves a lasting sense of wonder and zest for life. It leaves a lasting sense of gratitude to the many people who helped us through the most difficult time in our life. And with that, comes a sense of responsibility and desire to clear the path for those who follow in my footsteps. While telling our story sometimes resurrects old wounds, the meaning of remission, for me, has indeed become re-missioning, or re-purposing my life, and if our story can help even one person in some way — if it gives hope that healing is possible — then mission accomplished.

Wherever you are in Cancer Land, may the force always be with you.

● ● ●

PART
II

TIPS AND TOOLS
TO GUIDE YOU

We have two options, medically and emotionally:
give up or fight like hell.
— *Lance Armstrong*

23. | GETTING STARTED

N o two adventures in Cancer Land are ever the same, but some things we all encounter: doctors, the health care system and enough emotional havoc to last a lifetime. Hopefully, you've recognized something familiar in our adventure that can be of some use to you. Maybe you found some things that you hadn't thought of before that might work for you. Maybe Alex and I did some things that were so different from how you would do them that they clarified what would work for you.

There's simply no single route through Cancer Land, but if you and I were to sit down with a pitcher of lemonade and you were to ask what I think are the most important steps you could take to achieve the best potential outcome, then I would tell you everything from this point forward.

The chapters in this section are simply highlights because there are many resources which expound on all these subjects far better than I can, and I encourage you to explore the ones that feel right for you. Where possible, the websites of some of those resources are included in the following chapters. Where the url's are miles long, they are on this book's website, along with many additional resources for more specific needs.

So with lemonade poured into a couple of nice tall glasses, here goes.

I'd start by assuring you that in the beginning, it's natural to feel overwhelmed and underinformed. Those first moments and days are filled with dread and panic. We're often unable to process the news, much less what our doctors tell us. Still, some people manage to dive right in and start gathering information. Others, like me, have brain freeze and crawl into a self-protective cloak of denial until denial gives way to resolve and action.

I'd also tell you that there's no right or wrong way to "do" cancer. Everyone "does" it differently because we bring our unique personalities, beliefs, coping skills, values, worldviews, needs and circumstances to our illnesses, not to mention unique characteristics of our cancers. And no one can predict what any individual will encounter. All I can tell you is to expect the unexpected: there will be setbacks along the way. That's why preparing for what we can prepare for can help us meet the challenges and feel less out of control when setbacks occur. Preparation can also influence our outcomes, physically and emotionally.

I would also tell you that while cancer doesn't give us a choice about becoming a patient, we do have a choice about what kind of patient we will be. These next chapters can help you make that choice. They're not meant to tell you what to do, but to give you food for thought as you approach your own illness so that you can choose what's right for you.

Everything I'm about to tell you is based on my own experience as well as the experiences of many survivors who've shared their own stories. The quotes at the beginning of each chapter in this section were made by survivors, and you can learn more about them and what they're doing in Appendix I: Who Are the Survivors?

If there's one thing that I've learned from the many survivors I've talked with over the years — survivors young and old, rich and poor — it's that those who fared better, physically and emotionally, mustered all the resources that were available and became their own best advocates. Many were told they'd be "lucky" to be alive in a few years. Others refused to accept the next recommended treatment and searched for better options. They talked with other survivors. They learned about their diseases. And they got second or third or fourth opinions. Everyone who has done it knows that having cancer and becoming your own best advocate can seem daunting, but disparities in care are a fact of cancer life, and they can be fatal. Your very life may depend on exploring all your options and advocating for yourself.

Where do you start? By getting organized. Cancer comes with mounds of paperwork, from medical bills to medical records. A filing system that works well for you — whether it's an old fashioned file cabinet, a notebook, or your Blackberry — will keep you organized. I started with a notebook, which turned into several. The first page listed the contact information for doctors. Behind that was insurance information, disease and treatment information, notes I took during appointments, copies of medical records, and all the bills that came pouring in.

Keeping copies of your medical records is especially important because each doctor or facility has a separate record for you. Your copies combine your records into a single, complete record that provides your whole medical picture. And the whole picture gives doctors the information they need to give you the best care. Not only that, your record is always available if you see a new doctor.

A change in schedule is inevitable, and cancer is time-consuming. Putting all your appointments on a calendar can help you plan around them.

And keep important phone numbers handy, even in the car. At the very least, your list should include your doctor's office, your hospital, your pharmacy and your insurance company. And be sure to know how to reach your doctor during and after office hours. To this day, I still keep that list of numbers in my wallet, and there's still comfort in knowing that I can reach my medical team no matter where I am.

Not sure how to get organized? Some hospitals provide planners that contain essential organizational tools and resources. If yours doesn't, you can order a planner from CANCER 101 (www.cancer101.org), an organization which has assembled the tools you need to get and stay organized.

● ● ●

We don't survive cancer by just sitting back and waiting for medical professionals to do things for us. We've got to question, to research, to learn. We've got to insist that our doctors give us the time and information we need to make informed decisions. We've got to learn the art of negotiating with insurance companies. We've got to keep track of those test results and make sure they get forwarded to the proper specialists. We've got to become our own best advocate.
— Carlos Wilton

24. | PARTICIPATE IN YOUR CARE

Medicine has come much too far and become much too specialized for us to be passive participants in our care and still expect to benefit from the best that medicine has to offer. Nor can we sit back and simply hope that someone will take care of our everyday responsibilities if we can't. Instead, we can assemble resources that are available, from the best science and technology to friends and family members who can help with the daily routines.

In other words, we can participate in our care. Often referred to as self-advocating, participating in our care means sharing the responsibility for both medical and non-medical needs and participating in the decision-making process.

I'm always surprised when I hear someone tell me that they "can't" self-advocate. Don't let the term intimidate you. Self-advocating — participating in our care — is not much different than what we do every day: we make choices. Should we have steak or chicken for dinner? Should we wear this outfit or that? And though not every day, we make big decisions, too. Should we buy a Ford or a Chevy?

This house or that? And don't we choose the house or car that best fits our needs — not the one that the salesman or anyone else thinks we should buy?

Granted, cancer-related decisions are much harder and the stakes are much higher, but the process is similar. We do some homework. We ask questions. We review our options and then make informed choices. And there's no more crucial time to make informed choices than when we have cancer. Indeed, whether we're buying a home, ordering dinner or talking with our doctors, participating in the process is the key to better service, personal attention and reducing the odds of a bad deal.

So in its simplest form, participating in your care — self-advocating — means obtaining the medical and non-medical help that you need by getting the information you need and by communicating your needs. Participating in your care builds confidence that you're making informed decisions, and informed decisions can help you regain some feeling of control and turn hopelessness into hope. Not only that, participating in your care can lead to improving the quality of your life and even to a potentially better outcome. And since nobody cares more about our outcomes than we do, doesn't it just make sense to become our own best advocates?

Along with many other resources, The National Coalition of Cancer Survivorship (www.canceradvocacy.org) has an excellent toolkit that teaches how to effectively participate in your care. Find the link on its website under Find Resources and look for the publication entitled "Self-Advocacy: A Cancer Survivor's Handbook."

● ● ●

Information is power. It won't make your situation better,
but it will make your odds of making good choices better.
— Evan Handler

25. | INFORMATION: HOW MUCH DO YOU NEED AND WHERE DO YOU FIND IT?

We've all heard that knowledge is power, but what constitutes knowledge differs from person to person. Some of us need to learn a great deal of medical information and others need very little. Understanding the effects of illness on your day-to-day routine, finances, job, family or emotions may be more important to you than understanding the details of your medical condition. Only you can decide what is essential. Either way, there are lots of decisions to make, and the more you know, the better decisions you'll make. In other words, when we learn what we're dealing with, we can deal with it better.

At the very least, you should know *enough* about your condition so that you can understand what your doctors are saying to you and so that you can help yourself and help your doctors do their best. This means understanding at least the basics of your cancer and its treatments, and it means understanding the impact of illness on all aspects of your life. By gaining this understanding, you can find ways to improve your medical condition and your quality of life.

Now for some tough love, or perhaps more accurately, "brutal honesty" because it may be brutal to hear, but to put it bluntly, ignorance, in the case of cancer, is not bliss. It can kill you. If you were training for a marathon, would you study your opponents' strengths and weaknesses or would you take an Ativan and hope for the best? Cancer is a marathon that's full of unexpected twists and turns, and it forces us to make uncomfortable decisions. Understanding our opponent is the best way to make the decisions that lead to getting the very best care and achieving the best possible outcome.

Sometimes we're simply too afraid to gather the information we need. Fear is a perfectly normal emotion in response to cancer, and it can paralyze or launch action. When it paralyzes, fear becomes an obstacle to obtaining what we need. But fear, according to a wise old German proverb, makes the wolf bigger than he is. Indeed, knowledge can tame a multitude of fears that invariably arise from myths, misinformation or simply not knowing — and with cancer, none of us ever wants to say, "I wish I knew then what I know now."

Learning about your disease can help you plan to ask your doctor relevant questions and make good decisions more confidently. Knowledge can help you find solutions to your needs. It can help you make better decisions and increase the chances of improving your situation. And it can help you gather strength for the steps ahead and choose the best path to healing.

I also know that learning about cancer can seem like an intimidating, even impossible task, especially when emotions, fatigue or medications make learning hard. That's when a personal research assistant can come in handy. A trusted friend or family member can fill that role.

And rest assured, no one learns about cancer overnight. As you've read, I started my cancer career in the equivalent of cancer pre-school, without any scientific background to help me. What I — and many others — have found is that it's amazing what you can learn when your life is on the line, and you don't have to go to medical school or even take a course in biology. What you do need to do is gather information from credible sources — and there are plenty of them. You just have to know where and how to look so that you can get the facts and disregard the myths, misinformation and fallacies that abound.

These days, most of us head straight to the Internet for information, but the web can be just as harmful as it is helpful because anybody can publish anything. Out of context information can be misleading, sources can be biased, and bad information — or even too much of it — can compound the trauma of cancer. And there is so much information on the web that it can be overwhelming, not to mention downright scary.

You may recall that I found that out the hard way. Early in my cancer career, I was simply too new at having cancer to fully understand what I was reading, and looking back now at what I printed off then, I see that much of the information was already old and out of date. Some was flat out wrong.

So what are some reliable sites? The National Cancer Institute (www.cancer.gov), the American Society of Clinical Oncology (www.cancer.net), and major medical centers are great places to start. If you stay on sites like these, you'll begin to see that they are saying the same things, so if you later read something completely different, you'll recognize it as a red flag.

Reliable sites tell you who operates the site and who is responsible for content. For example, the website of the American Society of Clinical Oncology discloses who sits on the editorial board, and disease-specific fact sheets from the Leukemia and Lymphoma Society identify the expert who reviewed the information. Credentials do matter.

You'll also want to ask yourself where the site gets its information. Is it someone's opinion or it is based on fact? If it's written by a non-scientist, is it reviewed by an expert? Reliable sites often refer to studies so that content is backed up by scientific data. And dates on studies are relevant. The world of cancer changes rapidly, so studies that were made ten or twenty years ago are probably out of date.

Reliable sites provide contact information and identify the organization which operates it. Still, financial backing can influence how information is presented. For example, some sites are fully supported by advertising. Others are operated by pharmaceutical companies or by for-profit treatment centers. This doesn't mean that the sites are bad. It simply means they may have an agenda — such as selling you their drug or service. Beware of any site that charges a membership fee.

Links can take you to different sites which may not have the same criteria as the one you left, so each should be evaluated individually.

And if you read something that sounds too good to be true, it probably is. Beware of Internet snake oil salesmen who prey on the fears and vulnerabilities of cancer patients and their families. Unfortunately, charlatans are out there. You can avoid them if you're careful. Not only can bad information harm you, but if your doctor has to spend time undoing bogus information, that's valuable time lost. And we all know that there's precious little time with our doctors.

And one more thing. Whether you read it or hear it, how information is presented, and by whom, can affect how you interpret the facts. Consider, for example, these two statements: "This treatment may cause long term side effects and it might not work," and "All treatments carry a risk of long term side effects, including this one, but it may give you the best chance for the longest remission." Both statements could be referring to the same treatment, but could lead you to different conclusions.

● ● ●

Once you get over the initial shock of the diagnosis, you have to go into motion and educate yourself about the disease and your options. Being a knowledgeable and active patient makes a significant difference.
— *Scott Seaman*

26. | LEARN THE LINGO

Unless we happened to choose a career in the medical field, most of us gave up learning medical terminology in high school health or college biology. Then we get cancer and come face to face with big, incomprehensible words that we've done just fine without knowing our whole lives. It's like going to a foreign land without knowing the language and being unable to understand the answer when we ask for directions — and if we don't understand the lingo in Cancer Land, we may get to the wrong place. Since healing is our destination, it helps to understand how to get there. That means learning at least some Medicalese.

Early in my cancer career, you'll remember that I bitterly complained about learning this new language. If I was supposed to be impressed by big words, I wasn't. On the contrary, I was frustrated that I had to spend hours pouring through medical dictionaries just to understand what was happening where in my body, and I bitterly complained to Alex that Medicalese might as well be Greek.

Well, it is. Partly. The language of medicine is mostly based on Greek and Latin words. Medicalese began more than two thousand years ago when the Greek physician Hippocrates (460-370 BC) coined the word carcinoma, from the Greek word "karkinos," meaning crab, and the suffix "-oma," meaning growth. He used the word to describe ulcer-forming tumors and chose "karkinos" because the tumors resembled the form of a crab.

Hence, Medicalese started so long ago that it's unlikely to morph into something we can easily understand. Alas, it will only add more incomprehensible words to its lexicon, but that doesn't mean we can't master it. We can. And learning it doesn't have to be as hard as I made it in the beginning when I spent more time griping than grasping. In my own self-defense, I was initially too paralyzed to absorb anything, but it didn't take long to figure out that knowing the language makes navigating through Cancer Land a lot easier. It also helps us feel more in control of our destinies because we can make better decisions when we understand the lingo.

So how do we learn it? One word at a time. The National Institutes of Health has an excellent online medical dictionary with easy-to-understand definitions of any medical term. (www.medlineplus.gov)

Additionally, our doctors know that we're not fluent in their language. I've found that some are better than others at translating Medicalese into lay language, but most will do their best if only we ask. I've even asked doctors to draw me a picture and have yet to be refused. And nurses are great translators, too. The point is, when we have a devastating illness like cancer, it's not the time to be shy about asking for translations — once, twice or however many times it takes.

Just like learning about cancer, learning Medicalese can seem daunting, but it is possible, even lacking a medical background. And there's good reason for learning it: you'll be better equipped to have meaningful discussions with your medical team and they'll be able to take better care of you. Isn't that enough of a reason to start translating those 36-syllable words you never wanted to know?

● ● ●

People comparison shop for sofas, TVs, and cars as though their
life depends on the purchase. Why wouldn't you do the same
when your life actually does depend on it?
Always, always, always get a second opinion.
— Kairol Rosenthal

27. | GET A SECOND OPINION

I f you read Chapter 21, then you already know how I feel about getting a second opinion. Simply stated, it can save your life. But many people worry that getting a second opinion is checking up on their doctor. That's not the case at all.

The fact is, medical decisions often boil down to judgment, and different doctors may arrive at different conclusions. In some cases, they could all be right, medically speaking, but it may not be the *most* right for your particular situation. All doctors — even specialists — have personal preferences based on their own experiences, and they tend to recommend what they know best. This is simply a function of being human. For example, a physician who specializes in transplants is more likely to recommend a transplant than a physician who hasn't performed one. Or a physician who hasn't used a particular treatment may discourage it because he hasn't seen success in his own patients, but a physician who has used it and seen success may be more enthusiastic.

Additionally, the field of cancer is changing rapidly and new studies are appearing almost daily. As a result of the explosion of medical knowledge in recent years, no one doctor can possibly keep up with all the nuances of every type of cancer or all the new and emerging treatments. Even specialists may specialize within a specialty. For example, a hematologist/oncologist may specialize in treating a particular type of leukemia rather than all the blood cancers. It's only logical that specialists who see particular types of cancers day in and day out have more experience than general oncologists who treat all kinds of cancer and who can't possibly know the subtleties of cancers and treatments that they've never, or rarely, seen or prescribed.

Just as experience and knowledge matters in everything, it especially matters when our lives are at stake. To put it bluntly, if your doctor has little or no experience in treating your particular type of cancer, it's a risk to put all your confidence in him. And the only way to find out how many cases he's treated is to speak up and ask. As Ronald Reagan said, "Trust, but verify."

Unless your doctor happened to write the book on your particular type of cancer, a diagnosis of cancer — or a relapse — is not the time to remain blindly loyal to doctors just because we know them, like them, or belong to the same organizations or clubs. Doctors can only bring to the table what they have seen, done or read — and if they run out of ideas, so, too, do our options.

The key to getting a useful second opinion is to seek one from a specialist with more expertise and who practices at a larger center with more patients. It doesn't mean that you can't go back to your original doctor. Of course you can. But you'll go back with a new perspective, more knowledge about your condition, a potentially new treatment option, or reassurance and confidence in the treatment you choose.

Comprehensive cancer centers designated by the National Cancer Institute (NCI) are good places to begin looking for a second opinion. As of this writing, there are 66 NCI-designated comprehensive cancer centers in 37 states and Washington, DC. This book's website (www.adventuresincancerland.net) has a link to them.

Doctors — even specialists — are accustomed to patients getting second opinions. Sometimes they actually welcome them. And most insurance companies will pay for them.

If any doctor scoffs at the idea of a second opinion, it should be a huge red flag that you are a back seat to his ego. And ego will not heal you. Dr. Bernadine Healy, a brain cancer survivor and former director of the National Institutes of Health, has this advice, "When entering the complex world of cancer treatment, beware of 'I am God' doctors who, however well meaning, are saying do it my way or you die. Stop right there, and find someone else to care for you." It doesn't get much clearer than that.

The top specialists in their fields often talk to other top specialists. Even they know the meaning of "two (or more) heads are better than one."

In fact, these days, most major medical centers, and some community practices, bring specialists together in multidisciplinary clinics which specialize in particular types of cancers. Before multidisciplinary clinics came into being, a man with prostate cancer, for example, would see an oncologist who would recommend chemotherapy. He would also see a surgeon who would naturally recommend cutting out the tumor. And he would see a radiation oncologist who would naturally recommend radiating the tumor. Who was right? Maybe all of them. Each of these specialists was recommending what he knew best, but it didn't necessarily mean best for the patient.

In multidisciplinary clinics, various specialists work together and generally hold weekly meetings called tumor boards. The name may vary from one place to another — at Michigan, they're called conferences — but whatever the name, these meetings include pathologists, radiation oncologists, surgical oncologists, and medical oncologists who bring the perspective of their specialties to a discussion and review of each person's particular condition. Together, the goal of the board is to formulate the best possible treatment plan. In this case, several heads are better than one and you have a whole team of doctors working for you.

No matter where you're treated, it's reasonable to ask if your situation will be presented to a multidisciplinary tumor board. If so, then it's also reasonable to ask how many physicians are on the board and what their specialties are; if your situation raised differing opinions among the specialists and what those opinions were; if anyone recommended more diagnostic tests; if a clinical trial was suggested; and if the treatment plan was cross-referenced against a standard such as NCCN guidelines (more about this in Chapter 29).

Does a tumor board replace a second opinion? That depends on how experienced the tumor board members are in treating your particular type of cancer. Again, you have every right to ask your doctor how many cases like yours he has treated in the last year.

Finally, a word of caution: make sure that a specialist is really a specialist. It's easy to think that "Such and Such Hematology Oncology Group" specializes in blood cancers, but that may or may not be true. Remember Dr. Doom? The name of his group includes the words "hematology oncology," but doctors in his practice treat all kinds of cancers, so just because "hematology oncology" is part of a name doesn't necessarily mean that the doctors in the group are blood cancer specialists.

● ● ●

Listen to your body. Learn all you can. Don't be afraid to ask
questions and keep asking until you get answers. It's your battle
and you need to take part in saving your own life.
— *Lynn Lane*

28. | KNOW THY PATHOLOGIST

I t takes an experienced team of experts to correctly diagnose and treat any type of cancer. Pathologists are key players on that team. By evaluating tissue samples which are obtained through biopsies, they provide reports that detail the characteristics of our tumors, and oncologists develop treatment plans based on their reports. Thus, pathology is the very foundation of a correct diagnosis, and only a correct diagnosis leads to the treatment plan that will yield the best possible outcome. That's why the role of pathologists can't be overstated.

And for every oncology specialty, there is also a pathology specialty. For example, hematopathologists specialize in conditions of the blood. It's all they do, day in and day out. Might they be more experienced than the two pathologists at the hospital where Lisa was treated, pathologists who have the impossible task of reviewing everything from skin lesions to Pap smears?

Larger hospitals are better equipped to correctly diagnose because they have the sophisticated equipment to do so and because specialists flock to places that have the sophisticated equipment. Smaller facilities often send biopsies to outside labs, but they are not necessarily specialty labs. For example, Lisa's excisional biopsy was sent to a lab that had a very impressive name, but it didn't have a single hematopathologist, which is undoubtedly why its report was less than stellar.

And remember that she had two fine needle biopsies prior to the excisional biopsy? And that it took nearly four months to get a diagnosis? Might Lisa's outcome have been different if she'd been treated by a hematologist/oncologist with an experienced hematopathologist on his team?

And remember the pathologist who said that no "significant" lymphoma was circulating in my bloodstream? I shudder to think where I might be if my treatment had been based on his opinion.

When we choose our oncologists, they come packaged with pathologists, and pathologists are the most important doctors you'll probably never meet, but you have every right to ask for the credentials of the pathologist who reviews your tissue. Even if you can't get a second opinion from an oncologist, at the very least, it's wise to have a second pathology opinion by a pathology specialist.

There's no single place to find facilities that offer pathology reviews, but most major facilities do. A good place to start is at the NCI designated centers. You can find a link to them on this book's website (www.adventuresincancerland.net).

● ● ●

Even if you're tired, sick, weak, scared and angry, you must try
to do your own research about your cancer, or get someone close to
you to do it for you. Even if you have the most brilliant doctors
in the world, you have to become your own best advocate
if you want the best outcome.
— *Jamie Reno*

29. | EXPLORE ALL YOUR TREATMENT OPTIONS INCLUDING CLINICAL TRIALS

Once you have a correct diagnosis, you may have some treatment choices, even if all of them are not available where you're treated. How can you be sure that you know what they all are?

As ways of treating our cancers continuously improve, it would take an enormous amount of time to keep up with the changes — and that goes for doctors as well as patients. The National Comprehensive Cancer Network (NCCN) does it for us as well as for doctors. (www.nccn.org)

NCCN is a non-profit alliance of 21 of the world's leading cancer centers whose physicians are recognized as experts in diagnosing and treating patients with all kinds of cancers. Physicians are chosen according to their specialties to sit on panels where — together — they develop practice guidelines for the majority of cancer types for other doctors, patients and health care decision-makers. Each year, the guidelines are reviewed and updated to include newer treatments if available.

Physicians throughout the world can turn to the guidelines for help in developing treatment plans for their patients. And patients can turn to the guidelines to review treatment options for discussion with their physicians.

Using the type of cancer that I had as an example — follicular non-Hodgkin lymphoma — there are seven treatment regimens suggested as front-line therapy, but that doesn't mean that all seven would be appropriate for my specific case. Armed with this information, though, I could have a discussion with my doctor and potentially make a more informed decision about my choice of treatment.

The NCCN website has links to NCCN Guidelines for Patients and NCCN Physician Guidelines. Guidelines for patients are easier for lay people to read, of course, but they aren't available for all types of cancers and the physician guidelines are more in-depth.

You can access the physician guidelines simply by creating a free account with a user name and password. It's well worth it for the information you'll find. Even if you don't understand it at first, you can print off the pages that apply to you and use them to formulate questions for your doctor. And this will give you confidence that you've explored every FDA-approved treatment option that is known to the best experts in the field for your cancer.

But you may have more options than just FDA-approved treatments: those that are being studied in clinical trials. Every single drug — from aspirin to chemotherapy drugs — has been approved because patients partnered with doctors and participated in clinical trials. In other words, every one of us stands on the shoulders of previous patients who enrolled in clinical trials.

For me, the decision to participate in a clinical trial was easy because it gave me an option that I wouldn't otherwise have had. And as you've read, I needed every option I could get.

Likewise, a clinical trial may increase your options and offer access to new treatments before they are widely available. Of course, the decision to participate in a clinical trial requires careful consideration and understanding. Not everyone will want to. Not everyone can. Not everyone will qualify. And some are reluctant to participate in trials even if they know about them, but for others, clinical trials may be an option they're missing because they are never offered the opportunity.

A recent study in the *Journal of the National Cancer Institute* suggests that may be because doctors don't tell them. According to the study, part of the problem is financial: physicians who don't participate in clinical trials must refer their patients away, so each referred patient is a lost revenue stream. Don't you just love to be called a revenue stream?

Even physicians who do participate in clinical trials often lose money by participating because the administrative costs associated with government-funded trials are not, as of now, fully reimbursed, and it's becoming harder for doctors to justify shortfalls. The reality is that physicians must support their practices in order to keep their doors open so they can treat us.

Does this really matter to patients? Well, yes. If we recognize that reimbursement is a potential barrier to access, then we can't automatically assume that we know all our options. A clinical trial may be one we don't hear about. Additionally, there are many myths and much misinformation that surround clinical trials. Only by knowing all our options — and by getting the facts about clinical trials — can we truly make informed decisions.

Your treatment decision should always be based on what's best for you today — no one else — and you should always look at any treatment, including one offered in a trial, from a self-interested viewpoint and ask yourself how it or any other treatment can improve your medical condition. But from the perspective of a long-time survivor, I can't help but encourage you to get the facts about trials and to consider one if one is available and appropriate. Not only can it increase your own options, but since we patients stand to gain the most from medical progress, it seems to me that if more of us participated in them, then we could help drive progress forward — *faster.*

At this book's website, there are links to help you get the facts about trials as well as links to resources that can help you find ones that may fit your situation.

There is no straight and obvious course of action in choosing cancer treatment. Life's decisions are more like a tree's branches than a telegraph pole, and you need to branch out in order to flourish.
— *Brian Stabler, Ph.D.*

30. | TACKLE YOUR TREATMENT DECISION

Making a treatment choice was, for me, the hardest decision I ever had to make. Not only did I feel ill-prepared to make a decision that would affect my very future, but the choice was even harder because I had to choose something I didn't want in the first place. Sound familiar? It's not an uncommon reaction, nor is it uncommon for emotions to block out objectivity, but if ever there is a time that objectivity is needed, it's when we're choosing a treatment.

So how do we make the choice? When a reliable, proven treatment is available, the decision is straightforward. It's when we have multiple options that the choice is much harder. It begins by understanding the goal of treatment. Is it intended to cure the disease? Or to slow it or postpone a recurrence? Or to relieve symptoms?

As with everything in life, cancer treatments have risks as well as side effects, more or less in some than others. You'll want to weigh the potential short and long term risks as well as the potential benefits of each treatment. Will taking a particular treatment prevent you from taking other treatments in the future? What are the potential side effects? What's the remission rate? The cure rate? Only by understanding the risks and benefits of each treatment, and weighing them carefully, can you decide which treatment best meets your goal.

For example, if the potential for a cure or longer remission is greater, you may be willing to put up with more risks and side effects. Or you may be willing to travel to a different facility for a treatment that may be shorter in duration or for one that offers greater potential benefit. That's not only a medical decision but also a lifestyle decision.

You may remember that I had a choice of treatments and that Alex and I had no idea how to make that choice. We asked Dr. Kaminski what he would recommend if I were his wife or daughter, and he told us. If you're unsure, ask your doctor the same question. Some will tell you. Some won't. Even if your doctor makes a recommendation, the final decision is always yours and yours alone, no matter how strongly your doctor recommends one treatment over another.

It's also important to note that all known side effects are required to be disclosed for every drug. I know how scary the side effect list looks, but it doesn't mean that you will get every one. It only means that some people have gotten some of them.

Ultimately, your decision depends on the specifics of your individual cancer, the risks you are willing to take in exchange for the benefits, and how the treatment fits your personal preference, personality, lifestyle and beliefs. And the choice is always yours to make.

No cancer treatment comes with a 100% guarantee nor is any treatment a breeze. Most are downright hard — really hard. But you'll head into treatment much more confidently if you've carefully weighed the options. That means knowing *all* your options, including ones your doctor may not have mentioned or that may not be available where you are treated. Only by knowing them all can you truly make an informed decision about what is best for you.

● ● ●

*You are the central player of the health care team that can
get you better. Be a team player.*
— *Wendy Schlessel Harpham, M.D*

31. | BUILD A GOOD MEDICAL TEAM

Our medical teams include doctors, nurses (who can be our best friends!) and depending on cancer type and treatment, several other medical specialists, such as surgeons or radiation oncologists. It can also include social workers, psychologists or psychiatrists. Family, friends, support groups and clergy are part of our nonmedical team. Everyone has an important role, including us — the patients.

Firsthand, Alex and I learned that medical teams directly affect not only physical health, but emotional health as well. I would encourage you to build a health care team whose knowledge, experience and judgment you trust and in whose understanding and encouragement, coupled with appropriate realism, you find confidence and support.

But the reality is that top-functioning teams don't just happen. Building a good team takes everyone understanding the role that each member plays; setting realistic expectations of fellow team members; establishing and maintaining good communication; and developing mutual respect and trust. These elements are the foundation for good teamwork, whether you're playing football or fighting cancer. And when it comes to fighting cancer, good teamwork can make a bad situation more bearable.

My tips for building a good team follow. Use what works for you, add your own ideas and you'll have the makings of a great "Team You."

START FRESH: If you're new to cancer, your new medical team is just that — new. My best advice is to start the relationship off on the right foot: positively, not defensively. This can be hard if you've had a bad experience in the past, but don't assume that all medical teams are the same. They aren't. Just like every boss isn't the jerk you once worked for, every doctor is not the bad guy from the past. Don't let one bad apple spoil the bunch — there's too much at stake.

And unless you're extremely lucky, it will probably take more than one meeting to determine whether you feel that you and your doctor are on the same page. Like any relationship, it takes time and effort to forge a good one with your doctor and the rest of your medical team, but it's worth the time and effort it takes to do so.

FOCUS ON FUNCTION: It helps to recognize doctors for what they are — human beings with medical degrees. Like the rest of us, they have unique personalities. Some are warm and charming. Others are more reserved. Either way, your doctor functions as your personal cancer commando. As such, his medical knowledge is the most important thing you want from him. If you trust his skill, training and ability, you can find warm and charming elsewhere if it's just not in his personality. Still, it's important to feel comfortable with your doctor, and you have every right to expect to be treated with dignity and compassion. Cancer presents too many challenges to settle for anything less.

If you've set realistic expectations and done your best to communicate your needs but still feel that your doctor isn't responding appropriately, doesn't have good interpersonal skills, or the chemistry between you just isn't right, you may need to go elsewhere to find Dr. Right.

Nurses often pick up where doctors leave off. They can clarify information, answer questions between appointments, and usually guide you to sources for answers if they don't have them.

MAXIMIZE YOUR OFFICE VISITS: As we all know, most office visits with our doctors are short. To be sure that your questions are answered, prepare a written list of questions in advance, and take notes when he answers. This will maximize the information you get during the time you spend with your doctor and help you later remember what he says. If there's not time for all questions to be answered, ask how they can get answered. Can you leave them with him and will he email his responses later? Can a nurse answer them? Can you set another appointment to go over them? Or can they wait until your next regularly scheduled appointment?

And if possible, take along a trusted friend or family member, a tape recorder — or both — to help you remember what your doctor said.

SET REALISTIC EXPECTATIONS: Misunderstandings and frustration can be minimized by setting realistic expectations, not just about treatment, but about how your doctor's office operates. How soon can you expect to hear the results of tests? Will your doctor or nurse call you with results? Or will you get them at the next appointment? If you know what to expect, you won't be sitting home stewing because you expected one thing and your doctor's office routinely handles things differently. Make a list of possible scenarios and then discuss them with your doctor or nurse.

KNOW WHEN TO CALL: No one can plan for every potential glitch, but invariably, unexpected issues arise. Between appointments, we are our own best first line of defense against potential problems because we're the first to experience them. That's why it's important to know enough about your condition to recognize potential problems.

Talk with your doctor about when and why you should call his office between appointments. And be sure to know what constitutes an emergency and what you should do in case of one.

That said, if you're not sure whether a symptom is important or not, call and let your doctor decide. And if your instincts tell you there is something wrong, listen to them. It's better to have a false alarm than to ignore a symptom that needs medical attention or that may even be life-threatening.

SPEAK UP: Even the world's best physicians rely on patients to help them do their job. Who better than we can tell them how we feel or what side effects we're experiencing? Our teams can help us best when we convey how we feel, both physically and emotionally.

Communication is a two-way street. Not only does your doctor need to understand what you are saying, but you need to understand what he is saying. If anyone on your medical team ever says something you don't understand, don't be afraid, embarrassed or shy to ask him or her to explain it differently. No question is "dumb" if you don't know the answer — and don't let anyone tell you differently!

Speaking up when explanations or instructions aren't clear can also help protect you from medical errors.

DON'T WORRY ABOUT BEING A HYPOCHONDRIAC. I admit it. I'd had so many side effects and complications that I felt like a hypochondriac by the end of treatment. At an appointment just after taking RIT, I was in the middle of a sentence when Dr. Kaminski said, "Stick out your tongue." Startled, I stopped mid-sentence and slowly did what he asked. "Why didn't you tell me your mouth was bothering you?" he asked. "I just thought it was normal," I said.

It wasn't. I had a good case of oral thrush, an infection caused by my weakened immune system. Dr. Kaminski sent me home with medication and I felt much better within a couple of days. The point is that side effects happen. Our doctors are used to seeing them, but they can only help us when they know the problem. Take it from me: it's better to feel like a hypochondriac than to suffer if you don't have to.

BE HONEST ABOUT YOUR MEDICATIONS. Give your doctor a written list of all medications you're taking, including vitamins and supplements. He needs this information to avoid negative drug interactions.

While I'm on the subject, a cancer diagnosis often sends people straight to the health food store for supplements because it's natural to do anything we can to boost our chance of healing. Whether you're just beginning or have taken them for a long time, your doctor needs to know what you're taking because some supplements can increase the toxicity of cancer treatment or increase side effects such as bleeding. Others can decrease the effectiveness of treatment, and who wants to go through treatment only to reduce its effectiveness?

WHEN YOU HEAR BAD NEWS: Hearing bad news is an unavoidable aspect of being a cancer patient, and for us, bad news is a crisis. Delivering bad news is an unavoidable aspect of caring for cancer patients, but even in the worst case scenario, there is always something that can be said and done to offset bad news, and nobody deserves to be left hanging like Dr. Doom left us.

Dr. Kaminski and Judy often used a word I came to love: but. After explaining a complication or setback, they would always add, "BUT we have this option or that." No matter what the circumstances, they always found a way to offset bad news, and those few extra words after "but" were large doses of reassurance that often kept my hope alive.

Hopefully, your doctor will use "but" when he has to deliver bad news. If it's just not his style, don't be shy about asking what solution he proposes to diminish or solve the problem at hand. Even at the very end, a good doctor might say, "We've reached the limits of medicine, but we will do everything possible to keep you comfortable." Yes, there is always room for "but."

And one other thought: there's no point in blaming the messenger so long as news is delivered respectfully and compassionately and so long as it is based on the best available facts, not guesswork or assumption.

COMMUNICATE YOUR NON-MEDICAL NEEDS: If you're having trouble with transportation, finances, insurance, family stress, feelings or any other non-medical need, ask your medical team to connect you with allied health professionals who can help you find solutions. These can include psychologists, psychiatrists, or social workers who can refer you to community resources, help you navigate the health care system, and find ways to manage the day-to-day challenges.

Finally, you and your team will hopefully never have a disagreement, but if you do, know that even highly functioning teams have disagreements, but they work them out and go on to meet the challenges they face. Yours can, too, if you've built a good foundation.

The National Coalition for Cancer Survivorship (www.cancer-advocacy.org) has a booklet on teamwork. Find it under the Find Resources link and then under Publications.

● ● ●

I thought I was strong enough to handle anything, but suffered for months before asking for help. Give yourself a break and don't be afraid to ask for help when you need it, whether it be from friends offering to cook your dinner or help out with chores or asking your doc for help with depression. With help, we heal and get stronger.
— Mel Majoros

32. | PRIORITIZE AND DELEGATE

Most of us are much better at taking care of others than ourselves. And then we get cancer, which not only takes a whole lot of time, but also forces us to juggle between the physical and emotional issues as well as our everyday responsibilities. Bills still need to be paid. Kids still need to get to school. Meals need to be fixed. The toilets need to be cleaned. How do we handle it all? By breaking it down into manageable pieces, prioritizing and delegating to what I call the home team: our family and friends.

I know that it's not easy to ask for help nor is it easy to give up responsibilities that we're accustomed to doing. Subconsciously, I must have thought of myself as superwoman before I was diagnosed, but the fact is, nobody is superman or superwoman. Not one of us can do it all, with or without cancer. And with cancer, we have to learn to give ourselves permission to take some time off, to shut off the endless to do list. Others can cook, clean and do the laundry, but only we can help ourselves heal. And so what if the toilets get cleaned every other week instead of every week? In the scheme of things, does it really matter?

The reality of cancer is that some family members and friends may fade away, but others — even strangers — rise to the occasion and want to help. By allowing them to, you give them a sense of contributing while they help lighten your load. Think of it as a win-win. They feel helpful. You have less to do. Most people will need a little direction, so if you start with a list, you'll be able to delegate much more efficiently, whether delegating transportation, household chores, meal preparation, running errands, researching your treatment options, or keeping track of medical bills. Your list, of course, will change as your needs change.

For super-efficient delegating, you can create, for free, your own, private calendar that only friends and family can see at Lotsa Helping Hands (www.lotsahelpinghands.com), where you can post your needs, such as, for example, when you need another parent to drive your child to soccer practice or which days dinner would be most appreciated. People can go to the site, see your needs and sign up to do them. It's like a bridal registry, only instead of listing what you'd like for your wedding, you list what help you need when you're going through cancer. And just like a bridal registry, you end up getting more of what you want and need.

Friends and family are also concerned about you. While we all appreciate the concern, telling the same news over and over again is tiring and time-consuming. Caring Bridge (www.caringbridge.org) is another free site where you can create a private page and post updates. Your friends and family can read them and make comments. This not only keeps everyone informed, but also conserves your time and energy because you're not repeating the same story over and over again — and you can read comments at your own pace. I wish this site had been around when I was sick.

The bottom line? Identify as many needs as you can and look for solutions. Figure out who can help you. Remember that many people want to help if only they knew what to do, so be specific when people ask. And know that asking for help is not at all a sign of weakness, but of strength.

And if you're one of those people who, like me, could never say no to anyone who asked and who freely gives away pieces of yourself, gather your pieces and put yourself at the top of your priority list. I know, it's not so easy to do, but you may eventually find what I did: that saying no to things I really don't want to do became easy, and it's felt good to clean out the clutter in my life. Yes, there is life after no.

●   ●   ●

From the moment I learned it was cancer and I had to wrestle with all the emotions that come with that sinister word, this thought came to me, and I repeat it out loud to myself each day: Every day is a blessing. Every day is a gift.
— *John Kaplan*

33. | VISIT CLUB CAMARADERIE

There's an old Chinese proverb that says, "To know the road ahead, ask those coming back." In the case of cancer, those coming back are other survivors who, like native guides in a foreign land, can give you insight as only natives can.

We can help you find solutions to your needs, whether it's where you might seek a second opinion from an expert in your particular type of cancer or where you might find resources for medical studies, employment, financial or insurance concerns. And because we understand the emotional upheavals like no one else, we can celebrate your successes, cry over setbacks and reach out to help you through the hard times. And we may well be more objective than family and friends who are experiencing their own emotional upheavals.

What survivors can't and should never, ever do is give medical advice. If, for example, you were to ask me about RIT, I could tell you how to locate all the information that's available, and you could then do your own research. What I can't do is tell you that it's right for you because I'm not a doctor. Or you could ask about my experience with chemo, and I could tell you, but that doesn't mean that you'll have the same experience. In fact, you probably won't because every person and every cancer, even if it's the same type, behaves differently.

And let's face it. Cancer is lonely. No matter how many people surround us, we often feel alone and wonder if anybody understands. Survivors do, and our companionship can help combat your loneliness. Not only that, we're often more honest with each other than we are with those closest to us. After all, we don't have to protect other survivors from our real feelings and fears, as we often try to protect those who are closest to us.

There are many ways to connect with other survivors, in groups that meet face-to-face or online, and some organizations can pair you with other survivors with similar situations. I know that support groups aren't for everyone, and for some, like me, the term conjures up uncomfortable images. If I could, I'd rename support groups "Club Camaraderie" because that's really what they are — groups of people who understand like no others and with whom we can share our feelings without being judged.

For me, going to the "club" was like going to the doctor, but instead of getting infusions to heal my body, I got infusions that calmed and comforted my spirit — plus a wealth of information that helped me learn about lymphoma and make better decisions. That's very different from what I expected to find when I walked into that first meeting with a chip on my shoulder. Indeed, research has shown that participating in a group improves the quality of life by reducing loneliness, loss of control and loss of hope.

If you decide to participate in a group, the key is to find one that feels right for you. Nearly all groups that I've observed have their own personalities, so you may have to search until you find one with which you feel compatible. Online, you can observe for awhile until you feel comfortable stepping in or simply observe and not step in at all. And you can leave without anyone knowing you've been there. Another key is to participate when it feels right. Your level of participation will change over time, depending on where you are in Cancer Land.

Not one of us ever wanted to join Club Camaraderie. Indeed, the price of admission is high, but — whether you're a survivor, family member or friend, whether you're newly diagnosed, well beyond treatment or somewhere in between — every one of us is part of a diverse community where we learn from each other, care for each other and encourage each other, not because we must or because we stand to gain anything, but because we hope to make the experience easier for those who follow in our footsteps. Club Camaraderie: the doors are always open and you'll always find a valuable tip, a needed perspective or a helping hand.

● ● ●

Being able to laugh in the face of cancer lets you continue to own yourself, as hard as that might be, rather than ceding ownership to the disease. A good laugh reminds you that you are not your cancer.
— *Dana Jennings*

34. | FIND STRESS-BUSTERS

Coping with the emotions of cancer can be just as hard, or harder, than coping with the physical effects. Strong emotions and strong reactions are normal, and sometimes, panic and fear and despair are perfectly appropriate reactions. The key to emotional survival is to panic or cry and then to move on, but there's no one-size-fits all formula that teaches us how to do that because we react to everything as individuals. Additionally, every one of us brings our own unique emotional makeup to our experience, and cancer generally magnifies whatever personality traits we have. Thus, while some of the strategies that worked for Alex and me are sprinkled throughout our story, what worked for us might not work for you, and vice versa.

Coping with cancer begins by pushing back against the wall of negative emotions, and sometimes that's awfully hard, but pushing back is imperative to healing. That, of course, means finding stress-busters to help us push back, and each of us must find what works for us. Nothing will work all the time, but strategies can be learned. Some, including me, have found that support groups, yoga, meditation, guided imagery or listening to music helped to calm fears.

Other stress management techniques include massages or reiki or tai chi.

Pushing back against negative emotions can mean planning some fun things. Maybe you won't be able to sky dive if that's always been your dream, but you can still cheer on your favorite baseball team or catch up on movies you've always wanted to see or organize family photos that have piled up for the last ten years. There's always something we can still do and always something to look forward to. Ask yourself what it is and do it.

Even crying can be a stress-buster so long as we don't get stuck in our tears. Ask Alex today and even he will admit to shedding tears on more than one occasion. And never underestimate the power of a good laugh because nothing can lift you from despair better than laughter, if only for the moment that you laugh. These different techniques, or a combination of them, can offset the stress of cancer, and it's a matter of trying different ones until you find what works for you.

But sometimes, these techniques aren't enough. At any step along the way, cancer can make even the most "glass-half-full" people susceptible to depression and anxiety, and sometimes we're most susceptible when treatment is over. After all, learning to deal with all the uncertainty that cancer leaves in its wake is not easy. If you're feeling emotionally overwhelmed, highly trained professionals such as psychologists or psychiatrists can help.

Unfortunately, there is, for some, still a stigma surrounding mental health, and I've seen people try to tough it out on their own when they are in deep emotional pain. I've seen people who have survived cancer physically but who've been left so emotionally scarred that they're bitter and broken, almost as if they've died and are simply waiting for their bodies to catch up. It's heartbreaking to witness because it appears that they've given up on the very thing they didn't want to lose: life.

Of course these are not the stories we hear about. We hear the romanticized version of survivorship in which grateful, triumphant survivors run marathons, raise money or re-direct their lives. The stories are wonderful and inspirational and I love hearing them, but the cold hard truth is that not every story has such a chapter. If yours doesn't, you are definitely not alone.

If you're reluctant to get professional help for your feelings, think of it this way: we welcome anti-nausea or pain meds for the physical side effects of cancer, so if we think of emotional issues as side effects — which they really are — there's no more reason to be embarrassed about getting help for them than for getting help for pain or nausea.

And there's no shame in admitting that coping with cancer is hard. It's really hard. Getting the emotional help that you need can get you back to living your life.

Find links to stress-busters and survivorship programs on this book's website.

● ● ●

Everything that happens to you becomes a part of your life;
and you must choose to live your life; to own your life and be the
best you can be every step of the way. The art of survivorship
is all about how you choose to get busy living.
— *Matt Zachary*

35. | SUMMING IT UP

f I had to sum all this up into two simple suggestions, they would be: take charge of your illness and take advantage of the myriad of resources that are available to help you through and beyond cancer.

By taking charge of your illness, you are taking charge of your life. The fact is, from the moment we're born, there are twists and turns and ups and downs all along the way in this adventure we call life. We don't get to choose them, but we do get to choose how we respond to them.

With cancer, the twists may be twistier and the downs may be deeper than we've ever experienced. We may feel like we're on a wild and endless roller coaster. But eventually, the ride slows down and grinds to a halt. Whether we're cured or healed or whether our disease is managed as a chronic illness, whether we're physically whole or are left with reminders, we eventually disembark, shaken and weary, and we crawl, walk or run away in pursuit of equilibrium. But having ridden those chaotic rails — having had more adventures in Cancer Land than any one of us ever wanted — we are truly summoned to live, to make each day that we have the very best that it can be.

Undoubtedly, cancer is one of those events in our lives that can change the way we feel, the way we think, the way we see ourselves, and even the way we see the world, but there's plenty of living — *good* living — after diagnosis and treatment, whether or not we're free of physical and emotional reminders or even cancer-free. We can find it by taking charge of our lives, by taking advantage of the resources that are available to help us through and beyond cancer, and by focusing on what we can do rather than what we can't.

Andy Dufresne got it right when he said in *The Shawshank Redemption*, "You can get busy living, or you can get busy dying." My hope for you is that you are busy *living!*

● ● ●

APPENDIX I:
WHO ARE THE SURVIVORS?

All the quotes at the beginning of each chapter in Part II were made by survivors. Who are they?

Lance Armstrong is a testicular cancer survivor, founder of Livestrong, and author of *It's Not About The Bike*.
www.livestrong.com

Carlos Wilton is a non-Hodgkin lymphoma and thyroid cancer survivor and author of "A Pastor's Cancer Diary" blog.
www.cewilton.blogspot.com

Evan Handler is a leukemia survivor and author of *Time On Fire: My Comedy of Terrors* and *It's Only Temporary: The Good News and The Bad News of Being Alive*.
www.evanhandler.com

Scott Seaman is a non-Hodgkin lymphoma survivor and with his wife Charlene, co-author of *Battling and Beating Cancer*.
www.charleneandscott.org

Kairol Rosenthal is a thyroid cancer survivor and author of *Everything Changes: The Insider's Guide to Cancer in Your 20s and 30s*.
www.everythingchangesbook.com

Lynn Lane is a prostate cancer survivor and founder of Voices of Survivors.
www.voicesofsurvivors.org.

Jamie Reno is a non-Hodgkin lymphoma survivor, clinical trial participant and author of *Hope Begins In the Dark* and *Snowman On The Pitcher's Mound.*
www.jamiereno.com

Brian Stabler, Ph.D., is a non-Hodgkin lymphoma survivor and psychologist who often speaks about his experience.

Wendy Schlessel Harpham, M.D., is a non-Hodgkin lymphoma survivor, clinical trial participant and author of *Happiness In A Storm, Diagnosis Cancer, After Cancer, Only 10 Seconds To Care,* and *When A Parent Has Cancer.*
www.wendyharpham.com

Mel Majoros is a breast cancer survivor, host of "The Cancer Warrior" on Empoweradio.com and author of the award-winning "The Cancer Warrior" blog.
www.thecancerwarrior.blogspot.com

John Kaplan is a non-Hodgkin lymphoma survivor and director of *Not As I Pictured: A Pulitzer Prize-winning Photographer's Journey Through Lymphoma*
www.notasipictured.org

Dana Jennings is a prostate cancer survivor, *New York Times* editor, and author of *What A Difference A Dog Makes.*

Matt Zachary is a brain cancer survivor and founder of I'm Too Young For This.
www.stupidcancer.com

APPENDIX II: RADIOIMMUNOTHERAPY AND RESOURCES

For information about radioimmunotherapy, including a Q and A with Dr. Mark Kaminski, visit this book's website: www.adventuresincancerland.net.

You'll also find additional resources for a variety of cancer-related topics.

ABOUT THE AUTHOR

Betsy de Parry continues to live and work with her husband Alex in Ann Arbor, Michigan where she is vice-president of sales and marketing for their homebuilding and land development company.

Since her recovery from non-Hodgkin lymphoma, Betsy has authored *The Roller Coaster Chronicles* and *Adventures in Cancer Land*, written several essays and articles, spoken to numerous organizations, advocated in Washington for full reimbursement of radioimmunotherapy and for other cancer-related issues, and been featured on NPR and in *The New York Times*. She has produced and hosted educational webcasts and is currently producing a series of reports called "Candid Cancer" (www.candidcancer.com) to air on the PBS weekly show *A Wider World* beginning November 2011. Betsy also serves on the Patient Advocacy Advisory Board of the Society of Nuclear Medicine. Her experience with cancer was the subject of a documentary which aired on PBS on June 1, 2010.